T-Cell Chronicles

written and compiled by the
Xpress Yourself Group

OMNIGEN

Brighton

T-Cell Chronicles

Published in Great Britain
2003
by

OMNIGEN
Curtis House
34 Third Avenue
Hove
East Sussex BN3 2PD

ISBN 1-904164-07-2

Printed and bound in Great Britain

This
anthology
of
unbridled prose and poetry
is dedicated to
Father Marcus Riggs
1955 – 1998

Foreword

I am very pleased and honoured to be introducing this collection of writing compiled over the last year by members of the Xpress Yourself writing group at Open Door.

When Andrew first suggested the idea of the writing group just over a year ago, I was immediately excited by his enthusiasm and also by the great potential. I was in no way prepared, however, for the success of the group, and the incredible wealth of material that members of the group began to produce so quickly.

What has particularly impressed me is the range of work the group has created – from poetry to prose, humour to sadness, light-hearted to deeply moving.

It is also significant that people have written about all sorts of issues and experiences, some directly related to their HIV status, but much that is related to other life experiences. This clearly challenges the perceptions that many have that people living with HIV are all the same, and are nothing more than HIV itself.

Equally, some people have been expressing themselves through writing for some time, and for others this is a totally new experience. It has been great to see the group sharing their experiences and supporting each other to explore using writing as a tool of expression.

Andrew will be thanking all those that have supported this project elsewhere, but I would not want it to go unrecorded that this largely owes its success to his inspiration and commitment. On behalf of all at Open Door, I am sure I speak for all in saying that the writing group has enriched our work in many ways.

I hope that in reading the articles, stories and poems contained in this book you will, as I certainly have been, be moved, entertained, and more than anything, challenged to think differently and expand your perceptions of what it means to be HIV positive.

Nick Boston
PROJECT MANAGER
Open Door   June 2003

Contents

contents

1

AIDS is just a name

Mike Nelson

How did I feel when you told me the news,
that a Virus had taken its hold?
And 'AIDS' had come to you

How did I feel when you told me your fears
of alienation and rejection
through others' unfound fears?

How should I feel?
It is after all, just a name.
You, the person are still the same.

Our time together, once precious
now eaten away by this Virus
is now beyond value

Forget strangers' shallow words
what you deserve is love and respect
for you are the most human of them all

It is hard to love knowing there will be loss
knowing of the fear and the pain to come
but the biggest loss will be not to love at all

Help me to have the strength to face this together
and I will give you the strength you need
for together we will sail life's uncharted seas.

2

Aurora of yore although it is Fall

Marcello Evangelista

The day fades to evening
I look around
Nothing interesting
Just one bed, badly made, some stains on the wall
Peculiar stains on a naked wall
And the wardrobe doors are so plain, so warped
I look at this wooden floor and its small, wasted blocks
Wasted by slovenliness
And the lamp, up there on the ceiling, is also broken

Thus, I can say there has been no victory
In this war which I never took part in

I have never been allowed to take part in it anyway
I comfort myself

One more cold and damp day
When I do nothing as I am stuck to this bed
Thinking bitter thoughts

Why don't they just leave me
These persistent thoughts
Which I only maltreat?

I just retard my pain, by lowering myself
To observe all this mediocrity
That surrounds me

Aurora of yore although it is Fall

Dollorosa is the mother of my sense
She ignores other ways of loving Fall
And suffocates the dying leaves
As they attempt to chant as she screams

Exhausted wandering among wicked shades
I promenade stiff, static across remembrance
Dissipating time, which still strives to accompany me
During the rest of the day

Time is like the wind dragging sterile ashes
Once spread on the ground

I go on harvesting lies along the way
As well as ploughing dislikes and deceptions
Fears and pains of some wealthy penury
I become weakened by my penitence
As I hear the ashes moving in the silence

Staring at the garden, through the window
I see dancing flowers, moving in a colourful rhythm
Creating endless tones among so many contrasts

Another wind blows, arousing and more virile
It commands and kidnaps me
Clawing me away from bitter remembrance
Conducting me happily through the garden

Amazed that I become its lover
Sharing with it the thrill of new passions

I love roses with their warm rounded mouths
And other flowers
Which embellish this gallery
With their righteous virginity

Aurora of yore although it is Fall

I love the tiny insects moving through the herbs
Which spread all over the protective shield
That hides me from the obscure depths
I love the sunbeams projected through the trees
Bathing in light fruits, fertile and lush

I love all the different odours
Steaming up from the damp ground
The dew drops as they gild the garden in silver
They quench the sweet and delicate mosses

In my chrysalis I become a child
And still with wet lips
Completely fecund
I go on walking beyond the garden

Shortly the past was forgotten
I meet it again, feeling bitter and jaded
Drawing on idleness, it leaves and watches me with lust
I remember now my Fall's nights are longer
And I fall asleep of tiredness
And through this I can feel the night's breath
Caressing my face
As my body articulates as if in a dance
To gloomy Rhythm and Melody
That celebrates my fall

Not even with my best religion
Where I am god, preacher, penitent
The holy trinity
Can I possibly find shelter
For my imprisoned thoughts

Thoughts now ruled by fear and numbness
As if in a long symphony

Dedicated to the
memory of Jason B.

3

Back to work

Andrew Hanuman

(Sung to the dwarfs song from Snow White)

High ho ...
High ho, high ho, it's back to work we go
With Efavirenz and DDI
High low, high low, high low, high ho

High ho, high ho, it's off DLA we go
The man from the social said I was cured
High ho high ho, high ho, high ho

High ho high ho, it's like diabetes you know
Chronically fatigued with a rotten gut
High ho, oh woe, oh woe, high ho

High ho, high ho, my viral load is low
My t-cells are good but I feel like shit
Oh woe, oh woe, oh woe, high ho

High ho, high ho, sorry for being so low
After many years of this bloody war
After many years saying farewell
High hopes, no hope, high hopes, no hope

High ho, high ho, it's back to work we go
I look to the future with a weary smile
It's a better time, should not moan
High ho, high ho, oh woe, high ho.

4

Bloody Valentine

Andrew Hanuman

The process of moving on

You mister are one big thief
Took my love
And gave me grief
You offered nothing
But took so much
Don't want to see you
But I crave so much

I need to get you
Out of my life
Should I hire a hit man?
Cut you with a knife?
Banish you from my miserable kingdom?
Stick you on a train?
Send you to Swindon?

I'd like to see you squirm in pain
Make you dance in the acid rain
Cut your throat with a rusty blade
Watch you rot as the memory fades
If I cut you up
Would these feelings stop?
If I sold your bones
To the butchers shop

Die in terror
Die alone
Feel this torment

Bloody Valentine

That I own
I need your love
But you just ain't giving
So I'm sending you
To the land of the dying

In your lonely grave
I dance upon
You look so pretty
Like Eva Peron
But with no diamonds
Do I adorn you
Just a cardboard coffin
In which to chuck you

You could have loved me
You could have lived
But with your throat cut
I watch you bleed
A love not started
The dying seed
Goodbye my love
I wish you well
As the maggots eat you
As you burn in hell.

5

The dancing shaman

Andrew Hanuman

We looked at each other
The nervous men, understanding or confused
Out of nowhere he came, the beautiful man
Out of slavery I came, an addicted man
Yet I feel little fear as I open my heart, once more

I look to the sea, with head held high
I look death in the face
And he retreats
I look fear in the eye
And a kick in theballs
Could I deserve the joy?
Wherever it leads

If we seek to possess
Then we lie with fear
If we look to tomorrow
Then we lose today
I will lead my heart into a healthy place
I will cherish you and end the search

You and me, in confusion
We struggle with the fear
Like the monkey rides on the unicorn's back
The dream-giver and the warrior as one
Peacekeepers, healers
Sinners and saints.

6

Death comes to us

Mike Nelson

Some say I jumped from Primates to Man,
as the rain forest was no more
Others claim I fell from space riding on a comet's core
Conspiracies claim that I was found
In a Laboratory deep underground

Whatever my origins, I kill with stealth
First stalking the poor and taking their health
But who would miss them or care
After all there is 'population to spare'

Policy makers all wanted to agree
"It's not my problem, it won't affect me
Let it take care of itself
For it will never affect those creating the wealth"

5,10,15, 20 years went by, it made no sense
To nothing more than say, "don't die of ignorance"
But I continued to creep up on you all
Doesn't pride come before a fall?

To keep us quiet
They gave us a ray of hope and expectation
Some expensive and toxic drugs
To slow down its decimation

The poor could not buy them
So they slowly died of "thin"

Death comes to us

Governments decided on inaction.
For this was a "manageable chronic infection"
This did nothing to help those suffering
From despair and rejection
Few got any empathy for their bodily degradation
As few knew of this positive nation

Then I started to take the famous
And the "breeders"
And finally some of the mainstream voters
And "Sun readers"
So finally some priority was resolved
To this horror that I have evolved

Is this all too little all too late?
For that outcome we will have to wait
To plot the cases on a graph
To see if we have created our victory
Or our Epitaph.

For the ignorance that condemns us
Is not always our own
But belongs to all who inhabit this sphere we call home
The complacent should take up this fight
Lest I come and take them in the night.

7

Definition of life and love

Mike Nelson

Love is the truth of words when you told me
"AIDS is just a name"
Love is the shared understanding
That evolves from you being in the same boat as me
It is the sharing of the coping with an enemy
that is working from the inside out

Love is the promise made in words
to help each other pull through
It's the strength you give me
It's the mask of the victim
from which we've broken free

Facing up to reality, back on track again
Together under the shadow of a virus
with love and support the weapons at our sides

Love is knowing that now we are not alone
one and one make two – a hell of a fighting machine
It's the highs and the lows
that we see each other through
with a loving touch, a hug
And a few soft spoken words
that strengthen our mutual resolve

Love will hail us as two conquered heroes standing proud
together on the internal battlefield
Our colours flying high
The spark of love and life
still burning bright in our eyes.

8

TB and HIV – the devil's alliance

Eliza

I was working for the London Jazz Festival. I had terrible fevers and shivers at night and kept myself going with Nurofen and Paracetamol. I thought I had caught another bout of malaria which I had had in Africa five years previously. This was the only thing that the fevers reminded me of. The doctors seemed to trust my diagnosis without actually seeing the malaria parasite in my blood and they gave me a week's supply of Quinine Sulphate; a horrible drug which made my ears ring. It stopped the fevers while I was taking it but as soon as the week's treatment was over the fevers came back.

Back to St Thomas's and this time I was admitted with a high temperature. The next day the long list of tests began. Each one involved my being collected from my ward by a porter and wheeled away in a wheelchair to a different part of the hospital to be scanned or injected or x-rayed. They checked me for everything and eventually asked if I would mind having an HIV test. I refused, as I had refused in the past because I knew I had been at risk when I was in Africa.

Stupid really. It should have been more of a reason to have one but I did not understand the depths of it at the time.

The consultant and his team came back the next day and asked me again. They said that it was the only test left to do and they needed my permission. I so wanted to know what was wrong with me that I agreed but never really thought about how I would feel if it were to come back positive.

TB and HIV – the devil's alliance

Tariq, a very kind and overtired junior doctor, told me about the diagnosis – **positive** – with so much sympathy and sorrow in his eyes. I felt the blood leave my face.

Diagnosis: HIV and TB

These tests showed my viral load was over 300,000 and my CD4 count was 2. Most of the damage to my immune system happened in the few months before I was diagnosed even though I contracted the virus in 1995.

They call this dual diagnosis the devil's alliance as the TB drives on the HIV and makes it replicate much faster.

I did not realize that if I had had the test earlier I would certainly not have ended up lying in a hospital bed with TB and consequently would not have had to give up work and take perhaps a year to recover. I do not know yet how long it will take: I'm presently on month seven!

White, middle class and not promiscuous

I am a middle class white English girl, born in 1970, so in the early eighties when I would have had sex education, I don't remember HIV being discussed. At that time it was still seen to be a disease which mainly affected gay men. I certainly knew very little about it before being diagnosed with HIV and feel that people really should know more about this virus which is a growing threat to the population and can affect anyone.

I have never been promiscuous and have never used drugs. I spent a long time in West Africa and loved the life there, loved a man there and had good healthy sex with him. I did not think to protect myself. I believe that many of my generation would have behaved in the same way as we were not properly educated about HIV.

TB and HIV – the devil's alliance

Everyone is at risk

I had an uninformed idea about what HIV positive people would be like – mostly drug users and gay men. Visiting some of the support groups based in London I learned that HIV affects **all sorts of people**. I met such a varied mixture of people from every different walk of life. The horrible fact is that anyone who has sex is at risk, and most of us have sex. Many of us don't realize the importance of protecting ourselves until it is too late.

Everyone should know the details
to understand HIV and its manifestations

Probably few of you will understand the terms '**T-Cell**', '**CD4 count**' and '**viral load**'. I did not have a clue before this diagnosis. Everyone should know the details to understand how this scary virus works and also to better inform their decision as to whether to get a test or not.

A **T-Cell** is a type of white blood cell (lymphocyte) that identifies foreign organism. **CD4** is a protein on the surface of T-Cell: it is measured (counted) in blood tests. Hence the term 'CD4 count' is really about counting the T-Cells.

The HIV virus is a **retrovirus** which attaches itself to healthy immune cells and uses their genetic code to make copies of itself and replicate. The '**viral load**' is the number of copies of the virus in one ml of blood. The **CD4 count** (in effect the T-Cell count) is the number of healthy cells in one ml of blood. In **advanced HIV infection** the viral load will be very high and the CD4 count (or T-Cell count) very low.

Low T-Cell count facilitates
invasion for different diseases

The T-Cells are like the commanders of the immune army and without them the soldiers work but in a very random and disorganized way. The T-Cell count of a healthy person is **between 800 and 1200** cells in one ml of blood.

TB and HIV – the devil's alliance

The aim of '**Combination Therapy**' which since 1996 has been saving lives, is **to reduce the viral load** to 'undetectable', that is, undetectable by the machines they use. It actually means that there are under 50 (between 1 and 49) copies in each ml of blood, so the virus is still replicating but at a very low level. Once the virus is being controlled with combination therapy the T-Cells are able to start doing their job again, that is, repelling the invading diseases.

When you are discovered to be positive a test will be done to see how 'advanced' the disease is; that is to find out what the viral load and T-Cell count are doing. This will tell the doctors whether you need to go on therapy or not. When the T cell count falls below 350 it is adviseable to start combination therapy. The viral load will also be looked at. If it remains very low then it may not be necessary to start therapy.

The virus works in different ways in everyone's body and their immune system reacts in a different way to the virus and therapy. Some people are 'long term non-progressors': the HIV seems to have a difficult time replicating in their bodies and such people can go for years without their CD4 count being effected at all. They will probably not need to go on therapy and will lead a completely 'normal' life.

There is a terrifying array of illnesses that you are open to when your T-Cell count is low; mine was at 2, which meant that I was open to the whole lot. Scary Mary.

I was told my T-Cell count was 2 before knowing what a T-Cell count was. So I had very little choice and little time.

Everyone kept saying, "It's not like it was five years ago; there's combination therapy now, you'll be fine." But I didn't want to take the therapy: I was going to try to do without it. Surely some people did without it? I thought I had a choice. I had never even taken aspirin before; always trying the natural way to heal; always believing that I knew my body better than any doctors, after all it was my body and I had been living with it for 30 years. I felt that medical doctors were too mechanistic in their view of the body and I thought how much they didn't understand. But now I had AIDS. What a horrible word. So many people had died of it. Friends of my parents had died of it. Many people in Africa were dying of it every day.

TB is one of the major '**opportunistic infections**' or 'AIDS-defining illnesses' which occur in HIV positive people. Persons who are HIV positive do not have AIDS until their immune system has been so damaged by the virus that they get one of these 'opportunistic infections'. 80% of people who die of AIDS in Africa die of TB.

Ten days after diagnosing my HIV they discovered what was giving me the fevers. I had '**disseminated TB**' which is not in the lungs but in the lymph system and was hard to diagnose.

It is often confused with cancer of the lymph nodes which is also common among positive people. The immune system is so clever; as well as fighting off bugs and bacteria it also rectifies cells which are mutating weirdly, thus avoiding cancers.

Effective prescription

Within 30 minutes of my taking the handfull of multicoloured pills the fevers abated. WOW!

Now I felt so much better I couldn't wait to leave the hospital.

My friends cried with joy to see me back with them and I have only recently realized how scared they must have been at the time.

Thankfully I had some time without pressure from the doctors because with TB and HIV they start you on the TB antibiotics for 3 months before commencing with the combination therapy.

I was not going to start it though, I did not think I would need to. I always had so much faith in my body and was never ill.

TB and HIV – the devil's alliance

Alternative therapy?

A friend of mine told me about a herbalist based in Clapham who had done lots of work with AIDS patients both here and in San Francisco. He practiced traditional Chinese medicine. I went to see him at the beginning of January, only five weeks after the diagnosis.

I learned that most people who use him are also on combination therapy; I asked him why and he said, "It is the fashion." I was suspicious. He was so damning of conventional medicine. I wanted to find a balanced view. If I was to find an 'alternative' healer and turn my back on the doctors who were treating me so effectively for TB it had to be someone who I trusted implicitly. This man was too much defensive and did not seem to like being asked questions – just like orthodox medical doctors I have met in the past. He seemed to be hiding behind his knowledge and I was expected to trust him without explanation.

I have since realized that there is little explanation as to how traditional Chinese medicine works. It is mysterious and if my case had been less serious then may be I could have had more faith in that mystery but now I had to find something which had been proved to work. Faith in myself and my body had always pulled me through in the past but now I was forced to look at things again. I had AIDS.

He explained to me that he had lost many friends and patients to AIDS in the eighties; that there are herbs which have strong antiviral elements but there doesn't seem to be anything which has managed to control the virus. Despite being against medical doctors (probably because his work had been devalued so much by them) he encouraged me to look everywhere and find out how other people were dealing with the treatment. I left the clinic with a prescription in Chinese. And £50 poorer.

I so wanted to feel right about this. Actually I knew as little about what these herbs were going to do to me as I knew about what Combination Therapy would do. They are strong and have side effects too, and just because it was a mellow man with a pony tail and a nice smile who gave them to me, it didn't necessarily mean that they were going to heal me. He was making his living like everyone else.

I had begun to realize that I had a virus which had attacked my natural healing system. I could not take the alternative holistic route because it works on the premise that the natural healing system is more or less in working order and that the process of healing involves the rebalancing of that system. But my system was completely destroyed by the virus. So I could not think about my body like I did before. It was no longer the healthy, never ill body that it used to be. And this is when I started realizing the heavy and horrible reality of being HIV positive.

Which tradition of healing succeeds most?

I think many people disagree with taking antibiotics, avoid even painkillers, and are suspicious of doctors. But with AIDS and cancer it is scary and different. You have to look at which tradition of healing has had most success with curing us.

January and February were horrible months. I had a doctor at the hospital, who did not seem to look after himself. He always looked hungover during my consultations, which I just could not take seriously with what I was going through. I was in this horrendous position: I had to go on the therapy. And desperately trying to learn about HIV, and meet positive people to see how they were dealing with the situation.

To live ... or, to die

The fact that my T-Cell count was only 2 seemed to command great respect. " ... and you look so well," they said. But I realized that no one who had a T-Cell count so low had turned down the therapy. I didn't meet a soul whose T-Cell count had ever been so low.

I began to understand that it was not really a question

of choice. I was kidding myself that I had a choice. It was really about living or dying, which I found hard to grasp because my spirit felt so high and well and strong that I couldn't believe what all the evidence was telling me.

In mid February my doctor was replaced. He was the first doctor I felt I may be able to trust. He seemed to enjoy the challenge of my curiosity and questions and gently explained to me that there was all this exciting research going on, and that in five years time they would have all these new immune therapies and that he would really like me to be around for that. He explained about all the diseases I was open to with such a low T-Cell count and made me understand that it was just not an option for me to refuse therapy with all the damage the TB and HIV had done to my body. I needed some help to stop the virus replicating to give me a chance to fight.

So very many people had died before these drugs were available. Many people in red, gold and green Africa were dying without these drugs. The beloved man I caught it from had died from AIDS. What was I thinking about to refuse the therapy?

It would have been impossible to recover from the ravages the TB had done to my immune system without taking the jack and jills. But it was a lot to take on so soon after diagnosis.

Shame

To be ashamed of being HIV positive is abhorrent to me but there are many people who are ashamed because of the way society views the virus. They are unable to tell their friends and family in some cases through fear of being rejected. The challenges involved in being diagnosed and living with HIV are so huge that I find it hard to imagine how people without the support of their friends and family are able to cope.

It seems bizarre to be ashamed of living with a virus, which is probably the most clever virus in the world. We should be proud to be managing life with this condition. Why should I feel the need to hide my pills or be embarrassed when my alarm goes off? I am still trying to understand my position on this.

Confusion

I know that telling someone you are HIV positive is not a turn on. So, do I want people to know? Will anyone want to sleep with me again if they know? Is it better for them to see that I am a 'normal' person and to let them know once that relationship is established? Oh confusion!

Practical strategy

Now nearly two years after the diagnosis I am still adapting and feeling the ripples of shock. After spending many months very open about my HIV I have stopped telling people immediately because it is so exposing and alienating. Many people just cannot handle it. It is too challenging to expect people to deal with this as well as I have, and still be able to chat to me as if I have told them I just have a cold, or that I teach music. So I'm choosing my people more carefully and realizing that I don't have to tell the world.

I just take my drugs on time every time and give thanks for the **life** that was given back to me!

9

A difficult day

P J Greening

All the signs of spring were in the air and everywhere he looked the daffodils and tulips had begun to display a rainbow of colours around the garden, yet their beauty escaped him. The sparrow and the thrush sang as sweetly as if sensing and attempting to lift his mood. Here in his solitude, as he wandered aimlessly around the grounds, he felt not only physically sick, but his whole being – mind, body and spirit – was compromised, unbalanced and suffering.

He tried to employ some of the techniques he had learned to help him turn his mood, breathing exercises, meditations and visualisations. He began to repeat over and over to himself, "Just as I am, all of me, is absolutely acceptable and lovable," but he didn't believe a word of it.

The warm April sun beamed lifting rays upon him and the clear blue sky suggested a gorgeous day ahead, but he felt cold, and within, it may just as well have been mid-December, when the skies are darkened and grey. It was anything but a gorgeous day ahead. He listened to his voicemail.

"You have two messages …" He pressed 1.

"Message received today at 10.32 …

"Hello Darling, missed you last night, just wanted to say I Love you. Hope you are feeling a bit better; will come and see you tonight before I have to go out. Have a nice relaxing day mate. See you later."

It was his boyfriend. He deleted the message

"Next new message, received today at 10.43 …"

" 'Ello bruv, just got your message. Is there anything you need me to do? Do you want me to come and see you? Give us a call back …"

A difficult day

Again he deleted the message, and switched his phone off.

He sat on the bench and read the small plaque attached to its upright back.

'In memory of .... '

He was suddenly reminded of his own impermanence, and as he lit his cigarette, he could no longer hold back the tears that had been aching to be released since his admission two days earlier. Instead of feeling the nicotine feed his craving or elevate his mood, he coughed, choked and spluttered as he exhaled and allowed the anxiety, the frustration, the anger and the fear to take hold. Despite knowing that this was a perfectly human way of dealing with stress and worry, and a perfectly natural release and response to his situation, he couldn't help but feel like a freak.

"I hate you!", he screamed silently. "I hate what you've done to me, I hate what you've made me become; you keep filling me with so much hope, then pulling the rug from under my feet. What did I ever do to deserve you? Is this how it's going to be for the rest of my life? Why don't we just end this now?"

He smoked his cigarette down to the filter, something he rarely did, before wiping his sodden face, snorting the mucus that had filled his sinuses, gobbing discretely in the bush behind him, and making his way back to the ward.

He realised that this was one of those days that he had discussed with his psychologist at their last meeting. One of those days when he was going to feel miserable and depressed, and one of those days when the uncertainty became overwhelming and courage went out of the window.

Back in Room 1 of the Elton John Ward, Richard and Judy discussed the latest load of nonsense on morning television, as he lay in bed, feeling nauseous and in pain down in his nether regions. The nurse came to give him more antibiotics and analgesics.

A difficult day

"Did you take your combination this morning, Peter?" she enquired.

"No, I forgot. I mean I've only managed to remember every bloody day for the last two years," the voice inside his head stated sarcastically.

"Yeah," he managed to mumble from beneath the bedcovers, allowing the nurse/patient role to manifest itself even further in his consciousness.

"And did you manage to keep breakfast down this morning?" she smiled effortlessly.

"Yeah," he muttered.

"Heard you had a bit of a rough night with the night sweats last night," she stated

"Yeah; needed to change the bed clothes twice," he replied.

"You need to take these antibiotics and painkillers now with lots of water. Remember to drink lots of fluids, and if you need anything, just press the buzzer and one of us will be along to help," she instructed, as she swung round on her heels and left the room.

He sat up, popped the three tablets into his mouth, took a swig of water and swallowed. Taking tablets every few hours had become something of an automatic exercise. Reaching for his Filofax from the bedside cabinet and changing channels on the television at the same time, he tidied through the paperwork and looked at his diary.

He realised that it was April the 21st. It was exactly eight years to the day since he had received his positive HIV diagnosis. Uncanny then, that he should be stuck in hospital on the HIV & AIDS ward with 'Epididymo-orchitis' – a condition caused by an infection of the coiled tubes within the scrotum that store and transport the sperm.

He had never felt as unwell as he had a few days previously but he didn't want to appear to be making a drama out of what he thought was a fever or flu. His right testicle had swollen to twice its normal size and was giving him severe pain. He had soaked the bed with sweat and

A difficult day

become delirious during the night. Being and feeling unwell was commonplace and frequent. Some of it was a side-effect from the drugs. He often woke up cold in a pool of his own sweat, unable to grasp what was happening to him, his heart racing, confused over the nightmares, or having to rush to the toilet during the night as his bowels exploded in uncontrollable fashion.

Not wishing to appear a hypochondriac, if it was ever anything he felt he could deal with, then that's what he would do.

The cushions in the sofa were indented with the shape of his body, as the days of tucking himself up there were innumerable. It wasn't that he had an aversion to hospitals. Heck he'd spent enough time there doing his nurse training years and spent enough time waiting in one department or another as a patient. They say that nurses make the worst patients, and as he was an ex-nurse, made a very impatient patient. He had first hand experience of the stretched resources and the limits that those working in the caring professions have to work with, and as for the politics within the health care system in the UK, well let's not even go there.

Somewhere deep inside he knew he was in the right place and that he was on the mend. He had complete faith in the Drs' prescription of care and treatment.

He certainly began to feel a lot better as the painkiller kicked in and drowsiness began to take hold of him. All his friends were either at work or not in town, so he knew not to expect visitors possibly until that evening. So instead of fighting the effects of the analgesics, he allowed them to help him drift off to sleep.

He was awakened with lunch brought to him on a tray, but his appetite was poor due to the nausea he was still experiencing and as well as still feeling a bit groggy because of the slow release pain killers; so he slept some more. That afternoon as he sat up in bed having just administered another lot of antibiotics, he was aware that his mood had

A difficult day

lifted slightly. Maybe it was the sleep; maybe he didn't feel sick.

"Eight years," he kept saying to himself

"That's a long time to live with this virus. Other people aren't as lucky as I am."

He remembered a dear friend and focused on some positive thinking, replacing each negative thought with one that served him better. He let go of the fear and anxiety and adopted an open mind, a feeling of inner peace. He used some breathing exercises and affirmation. He was aware that he would continue to live with the virus, probably be on tablets for the rest of his life, and occasionally get an opportunistic infection. And even more often, he would have what he'd decided to call 'difficult days'.

Returning to the garden he lit a cigarette and inhaled, and, for the first time that day, he noticed the sun.

10

The fall

Marcello Evangelista

Fragments of a dream in a symphony

Immersed
In a sudden destructive moment
I fall through the support
Of the old sterilised world
Chanting with bitter breath
The terrible secrets
Of hidden pleasures

Dancing and singing in this long journey
Down below so distant
Profane abandonment
My temples bleed
Vile innocent
Lying patiently
Over the cloak
Of the heretic who hides

As I keep on falling
I remember old songs to Cain
Once forgotten
And I see distorted visions
In illusions that float

Six doors in front of me
Before I choose
Where the liquid pleasure and pain lead on
They both drip from my mouth

The fall

Showing me the way to go
Anxious
I deceive the banners of virtue
And go inside

Cruel.
I become abject

Wounds
Are
(Dis) closed

Exiled
I sharply confess
Like a scythe
Telling their heirs
Of Envy and Greed
Who now humbly bend their lustful heads
And praise the origins of man

Powerful and seer
I taste their bosoms
Amidst disillusions
Draining the melody

Now chosen,
Grief melts in itself
Devoted to time and ignorance
And part of my soul
Lies crying
On all the shame
That my heart contemplates
Consumed

During my sanest madness

The fall

While a dark vortex
Brings anguish and passion
With impure gestures
I bury my self in the dark

11

Hope and remembrance

Paul

I have lived with an AIDS diagnosis for 12 years. I find it hard to believe that it is nearly 20 years since I sat in a North London flat, the home of my one time lover and good friend, when he told me had HLTV3.

We at that time had no idea what this was, it had been reported that a group of gay men living in San Francisco had developed an unusual cancer – KS.

Within a couple of months of him telling me of his diagnosis he was rushed to St.Stephen's Hospital in London into the isolation unit.

It was a mad dash through traffic to get to him and I was physically restrained from entering his room as he did have an infectious disease. I looked through the window at this now skeletal figure clad only in a paper gown on paper sheets. It was unbearable to see him in this way, so I pushed through to get to him. Immediately the Hospital Management and Security were called. I knew nothing.

I walked to the bed and lifted this now very weak man, who had in his prime been one of those incredibly handsome men and it was all being taken away minute by minute.

I can only remember crying with him and through our tears I assured him I would always stand right by his side, at any time day or night.

I was able to visit him often but many friends refused to visit, thinking that they too might 'get it' – I carried on holding him, washing him and constantly telling him that everything would be alright.

On the 22nd February 1985 I called the ward and was told not to visit any more as they had located his family and they didn't want any other dirty queers near their son.

Hope and remembrance

On the 25th February 1985 at 5.35 pm I received a call to inform me that Tony had died.

I was not allowed to attend the funeral, neither was anyone else. His ashes are somewhere and I would love to find them, but after an extensive search, I cannot locate them.

From that day on my life would be changed forever.

This was going to be a life time of constant hope and remembrance. I don't really need World Aids Day to remember the nearly 200 of my friends that have died, as they 'walk with me' everyday. It is as simple as that. I can never ever forget. I will remember all of them; now, however, it takes me so much longer to pray.

I continued with my career floundering all over the place not able to understand why this wonderful man had been so cruelly taken away from me. Most of my friends were unable to understand my grief and anguish and at times I thought I would go mad.

I don't know why I took a taxi back to St.Stephens one year later, even less how I ended up on the ward where he had died.

A nurse, I shall never forget her, the girl with ginger hair and a face of wonderful freckles, came to me. She remembered me. I asked if Tony's old room was vacant. It was. Again, when in the room, it all came back and tears were unstoppable, only this time there was a wonderful nurse holding me. She said she felt I had a gift of compassion and understanding and could do great work.

It took a little while before I started my 2nd degree in counselling and a few years later to qualify as a bereavement counsellor.

Armed with this new knowledge and the increasing spread of HIV globally, I was on a mission. I was going to do everything in my power to get bereavement support for men, women and children effected and infected with HIV/AIDS.

This new mission sent me across the length and breadth

of this country, hearing countless stories of often cruel and debilitating attitudes and yet some of those still remain today.

In June 1990 my pension and insurances came up for renewal with a new clause, that I now needed an HIV test. I didn't hesitate. I think I had known for sometime that I did have it. This was confirmed as my bank then closed my account and forwarded me a cheque for monies paid in, with no interest.

By November of 1990 I developed PCP, an AIDS related pneumonia. After my third bout of PCP – my Doctors confirmed that I had AIDS.

The worst was yet to come. I had to face telling my Mum and Dad that their youngest son was now considered terminally ill.

Words will never describe the look of total disbelief and confusion on their faces. All I could do was to leave the house and go home. I felt I had hurt them beyond repair.

It took a while for all of us to adjust to my new-found health status and they both said to me that what ever time we had left together should be a celebration of life. And boy, have we done that ever since!

There have been many more illnesses and I have called on God to come and collect his loyal son and take me to Heaven to be with my friends. To no avail. I guess he doesn't want me up there yet. It has been getting very lonely here as all my friends are either dead or dying, until one day, he sent me an Angel.

I am blessed
This Angel is still here
Every day
All days
He never leaves my side
He always holds my hand
He guides me
He leads me

Hope and remembrance

I walk in his path
This Angel, this person
Doesn't have AIDS or HIV
He has love
A love that is true
Honest and kind
My living Angel
My partner of 5 years.

And we are going to walk this path until my rightful time comes? In my years since my diagnosis my beloved brother Colin died after a four year battle with AIDS. Followed by my Dad, four weeks and 12 hours later, of heart failure.

Can it get any worse?? Of course it will. However, we must continue, for this is what AIDS is all about – SURVIVAL.

With my words to you,
You have now become
Affected by AIDS

01 December 2002

12

If you're not gonna kill me, Superman

Emmanuel Lalopoulos

A surreal fairytale on Friedrich Nietzsche

Superman rubbed the magic lantern
And surprise surprise
An airy creature popped out!
I'll grant you three wishes, master, he said

Superman being very streetwise
and having fallen for a bad deal recently
with his mobile phone contract
decided to do a bit of research first.

These were Superman's words:
If you're not gonna kill me
will you make me look better?

I'll give you long golden hair
emerald green eyes and red berry lips
that men and women would kill to kiss.

If you're not gonna kill me,
will you make me stronger?

You will crush the stone
and lift the mountains
And when the night comes
you'll go to sleep with no worries whatsoever,
for you'll be the strongest creature in this word.

If you're not gonna kill me

If you're not gonna kill me
will you love me deeper?

Your heart will be soft and gentle
and love will be pumping in your veins.

You'll have
Love for the weak, love for the strong
Love for the sad, love for the happy
Love for the dead, love for the unborn
Love for the good, love for the bad
Love for the young, love for the old
Love for the deformed, love for the beautiful
Love for the inhuman, love for the human
Love for the unloved, love for the loved
Love for you, love for all.

13

In a normal day

Benz

I am sitting outside my place, in my garden, my own little garden (not quite, but it acts and feels as it is the real thing!), and I was wandering ...

I was thinking that I feel like a free spirit encaged, as if I want to do things, go places, experience things and life, but it is impossible for me.

Because of my life ...

Because of my circumstances ...

Because of my status ...

I feel like everything is being taken from me! It is not that sometime "I" did have it, or did I? But it feels that not even dreaming about it, is something affordable for me I cannot dream about going places: careless, exotic, dramatic, freer, wandering places – fabulous countries, exuberant peoples and landscapes ... That is not for me anymore. And I suffer. I suffer because something feels like nothing is being left for me. Not even the accommodated lady that wants to be married, have children, and live happily ever after! Nothing against them, but, "I" never thought to be or become one of them.

So what is left? Me, me alone ... and sometimes my imagination, which in a good day allows me to travel, to wander, to roam around the world, sometimes doing something good and useful; sometimes just enjoying the ride and making me happier, fuller, more intense, more alive.

But no, that is not for me. Because "I", am trapped. I am imprisoned for what my condition is. Because as a result I have to live where the circumstances take me to, not whether I want to be! Because I have to be surrounded by chaos, because someone else is taking the decisions for and from me ...

And yet, I feel as I should be – grateful. I am grateful.

I cannot compete; I cannot make my voice heard. I cannot make a difference ... not to even to my life ... and sometimes I feel sad, lonely, hopeless, and worthless.

Sometimes I feel like a little bird entrapped in this condition, with the benefits trap, at the willingness of the medical establishment, the mercy of the laboratories, the care or not care of the system ... Because I have to live by someone else standards, what they feel is right for me, whether they feel it is appropriate for me, whether they feel I am eligible or not, whether I fall into their categories, lists, or ticked boxes ...

And I'm fed up. I am fed up of being the justification for useless, uncaring and unprofessional people, who choose to think of themselves of being in a caring profession, because 'they supposedly care'. Why should they even earn a living out of my misery and still be portrayed as loving and supporting people?

I think it is about time to get the truth out there. Display it. Exhibit it. Carefully and meticulously examine it, as much as my life is. They should be accountable for what they say and do, and be held responsible for their actions.

I feel totally devastated when I am left alone in my own misery when 'they' can happily go home to their tidy or untidy lives (something they have the privilege of choosing). And what is even more disgraceful is the feeling that they left their little offices, or places of work, and go home thinking that 'that' was the best they could possible do, given the circumstances, and not even having second thoughts about the devastating effect that their decisions or acts have in our lives. They even should not be allowed to go home thinking that if something goes wrong (which there is a high possibility of happening), it is not up to them because they are comfortably wrapped in the concept that they did whatever was possible. Or, did they really?

In a normal day

I feel like swearing, and being very British about it, apologize for it. Something like "Excuse my French". Nothing against the French, or the British or .... anyone else, but if I have to be excused for something, it is, for being international. Because the truth is that no matter where you were born, or wherever you go, it is just the wrong place, or even the wrong time. Was there a good time place or time?

Whether you are in this country or in another similar to this, or whether you come from far away where the situation is even worse, it doesn't really matter. We, or 'I' am not worthy of any quality or dignity in my life because ... I just happen to be 'positive'! And now tell me, what illness is better or worse than mine? And tell me, how do you categorise me? On how I look, what studies I have or not have? Whether I work or not? Depending on my social, physical, or mental status????

It is only left for me to feel sorry, and apologize to the genuine caring loving people – a strange type of people in danger of extinction – for not being taken into account, not even in this little snippet of expression. I am sorry because their voice is not heard, their effort is not taken into account. And their little power and resources are diminished by the soullessness and rudeness of the establishment.

14

Insomnia

Andrew Hanuman

My sleep diary from 4.10 am

Dear diary ...

I'm adherent to the point of being anal. Friends laugh while I smile wearily. I set my alarm to remind me to take the pills. Post-it notes hang from the fridge: time to eat, time to take this pill, time to take that pill. No time for a crap, a dance or shag. Tick tock goes the clock, slower and slower, then bang its time again fast tracked to the next pill. The doctor tells me I'm a good boy: my results are very good, viral load is nil. Hip hip hooray! I'm going to live forever – like this clock-watching compliant slave.

Cd4 is rising – hoorah. Nearly normal now I ask? Good boy says Mother, keep it up, and keep them down.

I remember when I slept, how peaceful it used to be. I'd snuggle up in the safety of my bed, alone but for the faithful cat, purring, comforting my daily fear. Its 4.30 in the morning. I feel like a half dead zombie, an extra from some sick splatter movie. The white skin hangs from my sunken cheeks and the rings under my eyes like moon craters dark and dirty. Very few side effects, bit trippy, like being stoned, they said. Like hell, I say!

I used to dream of happy days, of fun and frollicks. I'd dream of love and sad times too. Dreams can come true, I was told as a child; now only the nightmares keep me company; how I wish I was a child again. For it was mother who would take me in her arms if the bogeyman came; she would fight him off, save me; I was safe.

Its 4.40 am in the morning and the bogeyman lurks in the corner, the cat is asleep and mother is far away. The sweat I lay in makes me cold, like laying on an iceberg

Insomnia

naked, paralysed by fear, unable to move or cry out. I manage to scream for help.

Its 5 .10 am I pull myself out of the dream, what the hell was that, I ask, as I reach for the light and knock my milk off the bed side table. The cat abandons me at this point, fed up of the screams and the thrashing of arms and legs. Very few side effects, bit trippy, like being stoned, they said. Like hell, I say!

Three hours till work – too late for a sleeping pill now. The two taken earlier make me groggy and tired, but not to sleep; just to make me clumsy, washed out, a shadow of the man I used to be. My sleep diary ... hmm ... like a speed freak I write frantically, scribbling my weird thoughts onto the book the nice psychiatrist gave me. Write it all down, he said, its therapy. It will calm you down soon. "When?" I said.

The cat runs and hides under the table as I stumble into the kitchen; she thinks I'm on drugs, like the happy old days of Ecstasy and Speed. I would Dance all night and make love into the dawn, with a handsome stranger. Higher and higher we'd go until our bodies crumbled into a Ketamine mess. Yes, we used sleepers to knock out the drugs; we'd feel shit for days but it was fun and it was a choice.

Its now 6.15 am and I've been up for 2 days; I feel like death warmed up. The morning sun burns my skin as it breaks through the dusty blinds. I will have my first meeting at 9.00 am: an important one, my yearly review, must keep myself together. I must not fall apart. How the hell am I supposed to hide my tiredness. I can't phone in sick again. Is it worth going back to bed for a while? Don't know for how long I can take this.

I should be grateful shouldn't I? With 8000 people dying every day of HIV worldwide, I should be lucky I've got the option of drugs. People are crying out for the drugs and I moan about my sleep. I ruminate over my western guilt, worrying about the poor of the world. I'm angry that I have options and they don't.

Insomnia

Fuck! It's 8 am. The cat screams for her food. Tuna and shrimp in jelly; it stinks. I look at the pills which are my breakfast and I gag.

Can't phone in sick again. Very few side effects, bit trippy, like being stoned, they said. Like hell, I say!

15

It came

Mike Nelson

First it came and took the starving,
disenfranchised and poor,
but we did nothing for we were not poor.

Then it took those of the developing world,
but we did nothing for we were already developed.

Then it took the persecuted,
the homosexuals and drug-users,
but we did nothing for we were not persecuted.

Then it attacked the outcasts and marginalized,
but we did nothing for we were in the main stream.

Then it took the mothers and their children,
but we did nothing for we were the leaders

Then it came for those who were left,
but we could do nothing for there was no-one left!

With appreciation to Martin Niemöller, whose famous poem inspired
this work. The culprit may be different but the effect of genocide
is the same.

16

It's a sick world

Andrew Hanuman

I recently thought up the idea of writing a short story filled with terror, human suffering and fear. I did not finish it. Why? Because it was too awful to be realistic, too much suffering to be endured, and I think a bit too sick to be believed.

I'll let you read a quick synopsis, though.

It was set in the present but it was a very different world. It was a world where a deadly virus had emerged. Initially it only affected the trash of society, prostitutes, gays and junkies. It also got the poor people in those developing countries in Africa, South America and India. But nobody cared too much for them anyway, so it didn't really matter. Many good, useful services were set up in the early years of the crisis. Many people pulled together and the medical services cared for its sick in the best ways possible. There was a culture of hopelessness and the suffering could only be contained.

Government-funded medical research was limited. It was therefore the drug giants who took control of the situation. It was also the drug companies which gave the people in the rich countries hope. After millions of deaths worldwide, suddenly out of the bleakness, shone a little light. Drugs were developed that would slow down the activity of the virus; people who had been ill started to heal and the death rate dropped. To many people, the worst the virus did was make you have to take the medication supplied and deal with the resulting side effects.

OK, they didn't work for all and nobody knew if they would work forever, but they worked enough.

Its a sick world!

The drug companies became more and more powerful; they manipulated and controlled the consumer free market. Only a small elite of rich countries could afford the prices for the drugs. There soon emerged a huge split in the viral community: simply meaning that the affluent of the world had life and hope while the poor had hopelessness and terrible suffering. Due to the huge cost of the drugs many services set up for people with the virus were either closed down or taken over by similar corporate organisations who offered financial solutions to a human condition, often replacing hands-on support with courses on how and when to take your medication; or people employed to advise you which medication to use next. It was a chemically dependent time.

While the rich continued to politically bicker and spend millions and millions on health promotion campaigns that did not work, the poor countries got angry. They were angry that they had been forgotten; they were angry that their loved ones continued to die. They too, wanted the chance to live. The drug companies became more and more involved in politics, coercing government policy and ventually finding a secure foundation in the government of the most powerful country on earth. They had the monopoly on hope: they decided which people survived, and they decided who died.

Some of the poorer countries attempted to gain access to the drugs by purchasing what they could afford from the drug giants but started making cheaper versions of the ones they could not. International condemnation bore down hard on them. The countries argued that if the super rich drug companies sold them at a price they could afford, they would be able to treat their citizens and would not have to break the law.

The most powerful country on earth went to war on the dying of these countries. They cared not for human sufffering but cared instead for their own profits. They threatened sanctions and costly legal cases. And the

Its a sick world

poor people feared that it would not be long before even humanitarion aid would be stopped. The drug superpowers also threatened the rich, sending out propaganda like, 'we are your only hope; look only to us; without your money we will not make them anymore; without us you will die'.

The rich citizens did not march, they did not protest, and many of those who were bothered could not exactly boycott them. Most of those who did care were dependent on the drugs, anyway, and without them there was the probability of illness and a return to the dying days. So while the holders of hope waged their war, the rich worried about blood results, the poor continued to die, the rich continued to infect themselves, fearing only drug choices, as the poor looked on in despair.

The tale I was writing couldn't be finished; I couldn't stomach the plot anymore. The storyline gave me nightmares, and if real, I would have felt shame. I threw the idea away, thanking any god listening that it was just fiction. It would never be believed; nobody could imagine a world so cruel.

We couldn't dance while others died. Could we?

17

It's you that counts

Graham Hamilton

Oh,
there
was a time
when numbers
were lots of fun.
When a 99 was an
ice cream treat on a
sandy beach in the sun.
A time when 69 was your
favourite pleasure with that
special loved one or someone
who counted on enjoying those
exquisite moments before the new
days of CD4 and
viral loads. Now
I am a number.
Not a name, but
one of those
c l i n i c a l
M-references
which tells my
sex, the year of
my diagnosis, and
the now recorded
figure of people
whose group I
have just joined.
Although I can
understand the
benefits of a numbered plan, it is important for
all of us to remember that, be we black, white,
woman or man, the numbers game may still be
won, if we believe we are someone's number one.

18

The journey

Peter Kim Lee Jones

The rise and fall of acceptance

To accept is to expect that things always change
So if you're sitting on cloud nine
Be prepared for the plummet
Back into the realms of rages and anger
Or the destructiveness of depression

Just as before, the journey begins again
Be strong
Because acceptance is just around the corner
Never underestimate the powers within
Believe in yourself and fulfil your dreams

The last goodbye

I lay, I sleep, I dream
Fading among my memories
Thinking of past experiences
that brought sparkle to my life

Reflections of the special people
that have flickered into my life
Remembering their joyfulness
Their love was so honest, so true

Seeping through my happiness
Comes the darkness rushing
Revealing the dangers
that will soon be coming

The journey

The future is clearing as I fear the worst
Saying goodbye in my dreams is easy to conceive
In reality, I resist, I fear the last goodbye

Whatever?

The torture I have can never be conveyed
in such a manner that people can understand
The hurt, the pain, that twist inside
disfiguiring my inner soul

Hate burns deep in my bones
determined to break through,
Destroying anything that stands in my path
without caring about my actions

Not completely knowing
the need to destroy or ruin my life
Still I continue not to confront my anxieties

May be I'm destined for a life full of loneliness
May be I'm destined to be happy with me
I and my self ...

Anger

The news sunk in like a sinking ship
Slowly but aggressively
I was being dragged ... dragged below the waves
Unable to take control of my feelings I hit rock bottom

As I lay in thee darkness alone and confused
Knowing that I failed myself somehow, someway
From deep inside my anger arises

The journey

Bubbling inside
I feel myself erupt like a fiery volcano
Out of control
Out for destruction against the world, against myself

My anger simmered, now controlled
Laying dormant but very much alive

Denial

I was told the news that I dreaded to hear
My head started to drift out of control, I drifted

Through the blackness of my empty soul
I could hear stormy seas
They were quickly approaching, smothering me ...
I could breath no more

Came back to reality with a bump
Even if it seemed like eternity
But a few seconds ago
I was told I was HIV positive

I thought why me, WHY MEE!!
Does god hate me?
Did I sin or lie
Why me, why me
It can't be me

Bargaining

With each passing day
I'm filled with new hope,
Because if I gave up smoking
I'll be able to cope
Then I might stand a chance

The journey

If I changed my diet
Even gain a few pounds
Indulge myself in vitamins
And cut the bad things
That I do so much like to eat
Then I might stand a chance

If I ran a mile every single day
Get myself fit and lean,
I could go swimming
Oohhhh, that's a good idea!!
Then I might stand a chance

My life would change if I changed all this
Would my life change if I did all this?
Please let it change my life ...
Oh please

Depression

I feel myself slipping away to a place I don't yet know
To be alone in the dark with no means of escape,
I'm calling for help, no one's listening
Feeling of entrapment overwhelming

Tears slice into my face
As I resign myself to my fate of loneliness and despair
With the pain ... oh god not the pain
The suffering is far too intense
for me to hold onto my senses

At the end of the tunnel I see a light
I crawl towards hope, away from the darkness
I feel a presence trying to grab me
to send me back under as I kick away
I inch a bit closer to reality ... to safety ... to home ...

The journey

Acceptance

I travelled the journey through shocking denial
Into the burning passion of anger
pleading my way past bargaining
Sliding deeper, deeper into the darkness of depression

Accepting is
appreciating the troubled lives we lead
understanding god
and why he betrayed me, my trust, my beliefs

Beyond the river and far over the hills
I catch a glimpse of contentment
Which was buried deep down inside
now rising upwards

The journey came to rest as I found my destination
I'm home in the sanctuary of aceptance

The mask

The mask creates a sense of wellbeing
deflecting away from agony the suffering
Underneath the pretence of my pride-filled mask
lays a tortured soul twisted and deranged
Hiding away the bitterness that surrounds me

Crying inside, but no one sees
the hurt that's buried deep below

The longer the mask remains
The harder it is to realise what is real, what is not
Through sheer determination I managed to survive
So the smile on my face, it's real, it's mine
... or is it

19

The leather bar

Andrew Hanuman

11.45 pm

I was twatted but still drug hungry, finding it difficult to
focus on the joint I was desperately trying to roll. The
ketamine was swimming round the back of my bloodied
eyeballs and I was determined to get off on it without
throwing up as in the past.

As the floor dropped a few thousand feet beneath me
I tried to look meaner at the man I'd spent half an hour
cruising. This man of mediocre looks was obviously getting
bored with the game I was playing and was cruising the
boy next to me. Fuck him, I thought; if he gets bored that
quickly, what's the sex going to be like. A wave of naseau
hit me like the tidal wave out of the Poseidon adventure.
I could see the fat 'Shelley Winters' at the bar; could she
save me with her friendly apple pie smile?

What the fuck was going on in my muddled mind, I
asked myself. Anxiously I sped away from the hard stool
and aimed to get to the dry part of the bar. Intoxicated
on a pot pourri of drugs I swam through the pretty purple
and orange pranah and beckoned the other survivors to
follow. In control and in charge, the rescuer leading the
other dispensable characters to the bulkhead. One by one
they would perish until only the superior survived

The Destruction club had been a regular haunt since I
had moved to London in the eighties. I lived near enough to
get there cheaply and near enough so the trade would not
moan about travelling. "You're guaranteed to get the shag
if you live close by," I slurred my words to the still-unrolled
joint.

The leather bar

"There's little worse than travelling half way across London to realise that the hunk in the club turns into the disco dolly in the cab, spending hours listening to him moan about his previous, failed relationship, gets demented on his acid and falls asleep. And here I am in Willesden with 50 pence, an expired travel card and a hard on," I murmered to myself. Thankfully the joint did not answer back.

I was seriously fucked off tonight. The results I got from the hospital were crap, dropping steadily over the last three visits. Time to think about medication I guess, time to think about feeling like shit again. Hey, it's better than death, I think?

I'd be stupid not to listen to the reason of my doctor, a good woman who tells me gleefully that she has not lost a patient for a long time now. I share her joy but I am also sad for the ones who could not wait, nor for those for whom the drugs haven't worked. Thank god they work for most. Ooh fuck, I am a bit twatted. Fuck all this for tonight. Do I really want to think about this now, in this state?

My eyeballs came around from the back of my head and I was able to focus on my surroundings. The music was as pop can be; chart hits and underground garbage remixed by big name DJs; hardcore mediocrity. Even with the support of the Ecstasy it sounded crap, like engine noises and sounds of bits of broken metal being thrown from a tower block window.

I thought of Ross. And hated what I had become, what Ross had done to me and what I had wanted Ross to do to me. Stephen the horny fuck made Ross cry as he came over his chest, became the bore, the dependable fuck. When the lights started to be turned off and Ross thought of bestiality in order to cum, I knew I was being sent away. I knew it would not be long before we would be saying goodbye. I just did not expect to feel so fucking empty. I did my usual therapy exorcising the beautiful Ross out of my system by fucking anything that would go back to my place following the break up. I would play a familiar game of self-destruct.

The leather bar

Although still trying to look hard I felt a tear roll down my face, unsure if the burning sensation was a result of the drugs I had gorged on this evening. Fucked up, fucked off and fucked. I sneered at the man who had resumed cruising me, after the pretty boy had pissed off into the backroom. "Bugger you," I thought. The man's face was less distorted than earlier but he now looked uglier. Fickle bastard, typical bloke.

As the men walk past I so wished I had a huge chiffon handkerchief to drop, to draw attention to the one who will do for this evening. "Oh thank you kind sir," I would say shyly, "looking for some unadulerated hardcore action tonight," followed by a cheeky blush.

I guess there are two possibilities at the moment. The horny but shy hairy-chested man; bit too passive looking, though. Or may be the shag from a while ago. Does he want a rematch? Do I?

I make it to the toilet unscathed, dying for a piss, only to be confronted by a group of men having sex. The lockup was empty for a change. It was a good excuse to have another line of Charlie before Patsy arrived. He loved his drugs and could sniff them out like one of those evil dogs at customs. He was late as usual, anyway; for someone who was a complete control freak you would think he would concentrate on his punctuality.

A really nasty looking man tries to push his way into the lockup. I held shut the door with no lock by my foot, carefully balancing my body to gain privacy while indulging in my favourite pastime. Pissed off by the intrusion I put my coke away safely. If I drop it in the stinking toilet I'll kill him. "It's busy," I shouted as he continued to push. "Fuck off and wait," this time I shouted loudly and with so much venom I wondered where the fuck that came from.

Coming out of the toilet I bumped into Kieran, another drug fiend. A dirty bugger; had a brief fling with him a few years ago. We only tended to see each other when we were off our face, and we would fuck for hours. We would mix

The leather bar

wonderful cocktails, Ecstasy, K, acid, coke and finally lots of speed to brighten us up. This was well before Viagra. How we managed a hard on between us, god knows.

But like all relationships where drugs are the main focus it did not take long before it all got a bit weird. He had wanted us to have a threesome with a mate of his who would have some crystal. I have had crystal meth only a few times and each time it blew my head off. After 12 hours even I get bored of sex. With crystal you can go for days. It is a passive man's drug, very difficult to get hard. It is also one hell of a nasty comedown. I can cope with moody Tuesdays but a week of paranoia is too much for this boy!

Kieran had wanted to bang up the crystal; it's what he and his fuck buddy did. I blankly refused adding that I didn't bang up drugs. He got the hump, turned really twisted and stormed out. Since then we only shared pleasantries. Queens throwing dramas over drugs is boring.

Kieran told me I was looking good. I thanked him and said that I felt it, too. I lied. I felt nauseous again and the sight that greeted me in the toilet mirror was not pretty. Eyes so black and deep I thought I would fall into them head first. I had that half shocked, half bewildered look on my face; how the fuck was I going to get a shag tonight in this state? I told Kieran that he looked good too, and added that I would call him sometime. I knew I would never.

I was feeling very cabbaged and thought I had better bring myself down a bit – a pint of Guinness usually does the trick – as long as I can get it together enough to order it. I hoped there was no one I knew at the bar, I needed to get my drink as fast as possible with no longwinded conversations or polite niceties. I would go back to my hard stool, get myself together and regain cruising. I really was horny; I wished Patsy would hurry up.

The barman was busy this evening which gave me time to fantasise about him while he was serving the sweaty leathered crowd. Out of my league totally, shouted my insecure mind. Heavilly tattooed and hairy, with a gorgeous smile and a very cute arse. What would he want with me, poxed up, drugged up and over the hill. Somehow I endedd up telling the sexy barman that he was wonderful at his job and how he had obviously been born for it. A vocation, I said, making so many people happy, on a regular basis.

Before I completely went on I could feel eyes burning into the back of my head. I turned round and saw Patsy.

"Quiet one tonight is it, love? GET OVER THERE and I'll get your drink for you." The barman continued to look bemused as I skulked off to my stool again.

"What do you think?" enquired Patsy as he put down the drinks and did a camp little twirl.

"What?" I asked.

"The new outfit," he replied with frustration.

Diana Rigg came to my mind instantly, but so did cat women: the leather jeans, tight with a high waist, with the small muscle top. It did not say dirty biker; it said Diana Rigg as cat woman. "Fabulous, really horny," I lied.

"Do you really think so," he said looking to the reflection of the mirror opposite. His arms and legs widened and he went into his east end lad thing, "Got em today like, mate. Alwight ain't they, for knocking about in."

"Yes they are alright, mate," I said, joining in the game.

"Your're trashed," he said in his usual school marm way. Patsy always had his wonderful gift of making you feel guilty even when you had not done anything wrong.

"Yes," I said indignantly, "I have had a few sweeties, very nice too, thank you."

Patsy pulled a couple of pills out of his pocket and swallowed them without a drink of any kind. That is hardcore, I thought. He giggled. "Better catch up with you then, hadn't I? Had only a few lines of Charlie and I get irritable on that. I'll save it for later when I'm having a shag," he said confidently

He was so together about cruising and picking up; if he wanted someone he would get them. He had this sort of gift. Like a shape shifter from *Star Trek & Bablon* 5 he could manipulate his look to attract all types of men. He could look like a real hard rough trade one minute then sensitive top the next, then from thoughtful and caring in the next breath to giggly camp passive fist me bitch. Wonderful gift, but his best gift was being all those aspects at the same time. Magical!

I thought about dumping my news from the doctors on him, but I thought better of it. Why bring him down? Anyway, sometimes he doesn't get the 'drugs and I' thing. "Think about your immune system," he would say, "I don't want to bury my best mate blah blah blah". No, I would keep my mouth tightly shut tonight. I know there is a fine line between enjoying the odd recreational and self destruction; and sometimes that boundary shifts very quickly, but, hey, at least I feel alive. Lost but alive!

Patsy went off to look at what was going on in the backroom while I was left to continue cruising. I did not want just sex tonight, though, I wanted something more, fuck knows what, but more than the the emotionally cold experiences of late. Trouble with having something more intimate means open and honest with the partner and I really do not think I can handle the disclosure stuff tonight: "Hello sexy man, and ooh by the way, I'v got HIV you know". I listen to myself almost apologise and assure the prospecetive partner that I am really very well, and very sorted with it.

Bollocks to 'em. Can't be arsed this evening. Don't want to be that vulnerable this evening. Reality is: I am not feeling 'that well'. Reality is: I don't feel very sorted tonight at all. I feel scared, I feel lonely, and I feel lost.

Patsy is snogging a man that looks strangely like Debbie Reynolds; don't know if he has lost his sense of taste or it's my drugs playing twisted games with my mind. Everyone is starting to look very ugly; don't know if this is me on one or coming down and seeing the reality of the leather bar. I'm getting too old for this shit, and too young to allow this to be my life norm. Playing the drugged up slut in the bar or

The leather bar

disco is familiar, intimacy isn't.

I managed to stumble to the bar to ask the still bewildered barman for a cab home. He smirked and passed a little piece of paper to me across the bar. "I'll get you one straight away, beautiful."

As if by magic a thousand chiffon handerkerchiefs fell to the floor while the club transformed itself in front of my eyes. Sparkling sequins covered everything like snow on a winter's morning and a choir of angels appeared at the door to the backroom, singing anthems of Love and Devotion. The curtains to the back room opened and the men inside sprang out dressed in chaps and jockstraps encrusted with jewels. They danced around the Destruction club to the songs of the angels. I was in Bollywood heaven. My sexy barman and I were showered with rose petals. He took me in his strong arms and gave me the kiss of pure love.

"It's outside now ... see you I hope?" quiped the sexy, smiling barman. The taxi arrived after what seemed like an eternity.

Oops ... back to reality. "See you," I said sheepishly. I forgot I had not said goodbye to Patsy ... anyway, he looked sort of busy with 'Debbie Reynolds'; I will call him tomorrow.

The taxi driver was not exactly pleasant but I did not care: I was on my way home, feeling glad I had not dragged a stranger home again. I reached into my pocket and pulled out the lovely barman's number. It read, 'Saw you at the clinic today. I think you are well, sexy. Could not say hi; was having bloods done. Would really like to see you for a coffee or beer sometime. Please call Chris. xxx'.

May be life isn't bad after all, eh. May be there was a little romance left. Even for this infected individual there are some more adventures. I am still alive – yes very alive.

20

Life!

Eliza

Getting my head around the dual diagnosis of TB and HIV and starting the jack and jills quick sharp

I am alive
And getting better!
Dare I believe I'm getting better?
Dare I?

YES I dare believe
I'm getting better
After months
Of antibiotics
Of fevers
Of worry
Of disseminated TB
All over my poor weak, struggling,
never-give-up body.

After months of
Are the drugs working?
Of fear of fatal side effects
Like life-threatening rashes and liver damage

I don't believe I need the drugs anyway
Fucking doctor giving me no choice;
The choice? Death or antiretroviral drugs;
Is that really the choice??!!

Life!

Read all about them:
Super toxic, common side effects include
fat redistribution ie, body changing into barrel
wth matchstick arms and legs,
super high cholesterol ...
Oh shit!

Why should I believe you
bastard fucking doctor?
I know my body, FUCK OFF!!

He gently explained
that he would like me
to be around in five years
when all these wonderful new drugs
would be available for me.

He gently explained
that my body is not what it used to be
I have a virus
It has been destroying my natural healing system
for the past five years;
My natural healing system is nearly no more;
I have AIDS.
I have serious disseminated TB
because I have AIDS
I have no immune system.
It has been destroyed
By the VIRUS
And I have AIDS

He gently explained
that the virus was winning the battle
Viral load 350,000
CD4 cells 2
Couldn't do it without the drugs

Life!

So I made my 'choice':
Always choose Life
And the drugs are working
After 8 weeks the viral load was 'undetectable'
CD4 count 40 and rising to heights unknown

The combination and I are in control
We of regimented behaviour
On time
Every time

21

Millennium Bug

Guy Painton

**Every action has an equal and opposite reaction
Everything we do has repercussions**

I hate New Year's Eve — always have done, always will do. When I was younger it meant lonely evenings with my family; special dispensation to stay up late with ageing relatives and absurdly cheerful Scottish strangers in a TV studio far, far away.

> Ding dong, ding dong ... bong bong bong ...
> A new year, a new beginning, a new life
> Except when you wake up everything's the same
> Everything we do has repercussions

Older now, with a taste for sherry and cheap cider — sweet intoxication for a sugar-addicted adolescent. A gay boy lost in a sea of straight men, stealing kisses at midnight, because we all do it then — boy on boy on girl on girl on boy on girl on boy. Forgotten in the morning, packed away with the tinsel for another year. "God! I was so pissed last night."

> Ding dong, ding dong ... bong bong bong ...
> A new year, a new beginning, a new life
> Except when you wake up everything's the same
> Everything we do has repercussions

Older again but still none the wiser. Picture a bar in a far-eastern country, stars and stripes and Liberty with her torch held aloft. "Bring me your starving and your huddled masses" — "No Koreans Allowed". Shaven-headed

Millennium Bug

farm boys with red necks and eagle-shaped tattoos, a porn fantasy. Turn the video off, this is real life. These guys don't fuck each other. They have to be told to wrap up warm in a blizzard ... Corn-fed cannon fodder for an arrogant nation, cheap medals proudly displayed in a trailer back home.

> Ding dong, ding dong ... bong bong bong ...
> A new year, a new beginning, a new life
> Except when you wake up everything's the same
> Everything we do has repercussions

Home again, but only just – a club full of strangers. Kiss the ageing barmaid (she's been here for years). Straight, gay, it's all the same to her. "I just serve the beers, love ... Happy New Year!"

> Ding dong, ding dong ... bong bong bong ...
> A new year, a new beginning, a new life
> Except when you wake up everything's the same
> Everything we do has repercussions

And now the big one – not just a new year or a new decade, not just a new century, but a new millennium. This time things have got to change – computer meltdown, a new order, a brave new world.

Forgive me if I've heard it all before. Forgive me if I don't want to be here. The sleepers didn't work, so try something else. Still with us? Have a dab, snort a line, take a pill, have a drink. Drug-fucked sex, unremembered sex, unprotected sex, unsafe sex ... a virus.

> Ding dong, ding dong ... bong bong bong ...
> A new year, a new beginning, a new life
> Except when you wake up nothing's the same
> Everything we do has reaper-cussions

22

A move forwards

Mike Nelson

I know now more than ever
since you came into my life
I'm not on my own
The walls of isolation
I thought had me trapped for all time
crashed down like the walls of Jericho
when you stepped up and stood by my side

When my feelings have taken a downward turn
and I am all out of sync,
when I feel pushed into depressive darkess
or into fear-painted corners,
I know your loving hand will reach out and help me
with the gift of love to pull me through,
to pull me into the light to be embraced
in the arc of warm understanding

When I feel like everything's slipping away
and I am taking too many steps backwards
I know you will be there to show me
the way forward again
and stop my head hanging down
so I can hold it high once more.

The love we share is so complete
it's made me whole again
knowing that it's wonderfully mutual
I feel too, that time at last will heal past wounds finally
so that I can let go completely
and fly free right here beside you.

23

My heroine

Mark

My heroine loves me
But do I love her?
What do I do?

I wake up dreaming of her
She is with me everyday
Will she be with me
Til I die?

I hurt when she is not with me
What can I do?
She gives me pleasure
When she is around
Will she be with me
Till I die?

My heroine loves me
She loves my friends
When she's around
My friends love me
What can I do?
Will she be with me
Till the day I die?

24

My mate Ritchie

Chris

Ritchie, my disco partner, was my mate for many years. He was outgoing, flamboyant, and full of love and generosity. Ritchie was never promiscuous; in fact he used to cringe at the sight of a willy.

He was a hairdresser
He was my hairdresser
He was my best mate

I won him a trophy once for a hair competition; it was kept in his mum's china cabinet. He then went on to achieve one of the goals in his life – to be a steward for British Airways.

Now he was my trolley dolly mate

Two years later, hearing he was ill, I knocked on his door. His mother said he didn't want to see anyone. She told me, as she had the rest of the council estate they lived on, "he had a tropical disease". The shame, the neighbours; what would they say?

It shouldn't happen like this – but it did. Ritchie died a year later, the result of this terrible illness, the so-called tropical disease. He's now in heaven, a place where prejudice and gossip don't exist.

I hope he's still hairdressing up above, after all there are many angels with long hair and wings that will need tinting or trimming.

God bless you Ritchie. I, Chris, your disco mate, think of you all the time.

If you're listening (you probably are, you never missed a thing) I might be joining you soon; there are loads of great dance tracks around at the minute, I'll bring them with me.

25

My travelling companion

Andrew Hanuman

A traveller on this rocky road
Many adventures have I had
To wondrous exotic places
Met the privileged and the sad

I've travelled many seas
In both calm and storm alike
To immerse myself in the journey
To the centre of the soul

A million different faces
A million different lands
I've taken many roads
To bring me to your hand

The pains slow me down
The aching takes its toll
But steadily I search for you
In the darkness your name I call

I came to many crossroads
Confused which way to turn
In my heart I've held you dear
Remember how your kisses burn

Like a moth to the flame
I am drawn to your light
Even though I am slowed down
I utilise my spite

My travelling companion

My travelling companion
Knocks me to my knees
The shooting pains of Neuropathy
A torture no one sees

I know one day I'll find you
My memory holds you dear
Through my pain and loneliness
You keep away the fear

Wait for me loved one
Ill be with you soon
Just need a little medication
To help me see the moon

*Dedicated to the
memory of Ray G*

26

Normal is
what you're used to

Antony Roberts

**I am a normal guy. I am the same as
everyone else. I just happen to be gay.**

Hmmmmmm ...

It took me far too long to realise that is such bollocks.

The penny started to drop a year or so ago.

I was having dinner with Belinda, a brisk and brusque
colleague of mine, and four of her friends. Like me, they
were all in their mid to late 30s, (oh, ok, 43 if you are
going to be fussy). They were all successful 'something-in-
the-City' types. Smart. Dynamic. Robust. They looked
like they could eat men's balls for breakfast – in fact they
probably did. Daily. Raw. Whilst still attached. Without
anaesthetic. They weren't the type to take prisoners, and
if they ever did it would be for the sport of torturing them.
When they were at school they pulled the legs off spiders to
watch how painfully they limped and hobbled away, chased,
no doubt, by a struck match and a cackling laugh. They
probably still did that on a bored Wednesday night.

And here they were, reigning over their few square
yards of power in a Square Mile tower; boasting and
toasting their successes. Their time had come. They were
riding their wave at its peak, wearing the medals of new-
millennium success. What they wanted, they got. And
when they had had it they spat it back out. They didn't have
time to swallow.

Aggressive? Fuck, were they aggressive! The original
tit-bulled terriers; with absolutely no idea of how overbearing

Normal is what you're used to

they were. It was all second nature to them. Birds of a feather stick together, and vultures work in packs.

Sophee was the worst. Yes, that is the correct spelling. She introduced herself with the appendix "and that's without an 'i' but with 'two 'e's", which even I thought was a bit heavy going for a non-dancing night. Well, ok, maybe not, but at least let's finish the meal first.

Sophee, oooops, sorreeeeeeeeeeee, 'Sophee' was the new one to the group. The rest of us had met regularly over the years. We had shared life's ups and ups together. There was a lot of shared history around the table, and, even though we would never admit it, that was reassuring. But that night Sophee broke into the circle and broke its spell. Our subtle changes over the years were suddenly exposed.

I swear this is true.

Little-Miss-Two-Es had just finished a dreary monologue on how her Hoxton flat had appreciated so much in value over the last year and how Hoxton was so much a more sought after area than Whitechapel. Frankly she may as well have said "Doncaster is so much more 'sought after' than Rotherham." I certainly have no intention of ever visiting any of them. Yes, I agree with you, she really ought to get out a bit more often. Property prices are just so last century. Besides, I had seen her photos of her flat. It is the scrag end of an old scrap yard; exposed brick for exposed pretensions.

During cocktails Sophee had shared with us the exciting news of her impending promotion. We were pleased for her.

As we studied the menu Sophee updated us on how stupid her colleagues had been today. Wasn't it so obvious? Only obvious to someone with your talent, dear. We marvelled at her.

During my sweet Thai soup Sophee soured us with the horror of the latest price of a Persian Blue cat. You would have thought that as she was buying four they would have

Normal is what you're used to

given her a discount. Well, wouldn't you? Fortunately she could afford it, but it was the principle of the thing that had upset her so much. Oh how we sympathised with her and admired her principled stance. Well done, love.

And she knew both when and how to stand her ground. Unfortunately so did the cute waiter when she flicked him and his so-called Vodka-Martini away. I mean, really! Who would dream of cocktail-sticking the olives green, green and then black. All green is fine. All black is fine. Green-black-green is fine, as is black-green-black. But green-green-black! Oh pur-leeeeeeeeese! And if people like her didn't insist on it being done properly then this place would just go to seed as quickly as all the others had done. We were grateful to her. Thank you, darling.

By the time the main course arrived she was getting on my tits. By the time the main course left she was clamped to them and making them bleed. Normally that would have been fun, but not here, not now and, most certainly, not with her.

I studied the other diners with eyes ready to roll in conspiratorial unison. But they weren't up for that. They were genuinely interested. Indeed they were matching Little-Miss-Two-Es story for story, step for step, half-truth for half-truth.

I was bored, but they were enraptured. Once upon a time this had been my peer group, my circle of fellow-journeymen, but not now. This woman was a living reflection of what the group had become. Those knowing doubts I had felt over the last few dinners were suddenly crystallised and summarised in this spectre, haunting before us; the ghost of our Christmases yet to come. Maybe I had been getting softer in my old age, or maybe they had been getting harder. Either way there was space between us which had never been there before.

"Sophe?" I asked, deliberately mis-pronouncing her name for sheer devilment, "have you always been this competitive?"

Normal is what you're used to

She was aghast. Indeed she was as aghast as she was ghastly. She was very aghast.

"Excuse me Rob!" She grasped her hand to her chest, not in mock-shock, but this was real thing. "What did you just say about me?"

She fixed me a look and smouldered indignantly. I think she wanted to fire me on the spot, and was frustrated only by the point of detail that I didn't work for her. As her eyes glared and her nostrils flared I wondered if she was about to offer me a very well paid job just so she could have the satisfaction of sacking me from it.

"You think I am competitive?"

As if ...

"Erm ... How can I say this without causing any offence?" I stammered, hammered by her glare. Really I meant "how can I say this with causing as much offence as possible you obnoxious bitch".

"Erm ... yes Sophee, I do think you are rather competitive. Indeed I think you are very competitive". I could have added my other thoughts about her, but this was enough to be getting on with.

"Rob."

Little-Miss-Two-E's dropped her voice and slowed her words. She deliberately turned to face me. I was so grateful. It meant even an idiot like me with a first class honours from Cambridge could understand what she was about to say. If I struggled with any big words then I could at least try and lip-read what she was saying. To help me further she reached across to rest her hand reassuringly, (not), on mine. With a partly disguised look of pity she actually patted my fingers as she explained "Rob, you really don't understand do you? I am the *least* competitive person *ever* ..."

I looked to Belinda to rescue my sanity with an ironic appreciation. But Belinda smiled smugly, safe in the knowledge that she was even less competitive than Little-Miss-Two-Es.

Normal is what you're used to

You see, the point is that, once, I thought I had a lot in common with these girls. Indeed I did have a lot in common. We are all of the same age; we all work in a similar field. We could probably all name John Noakes's sheep dog from Blue Peter in the early 1970s. None of us had kids and, to be honest of all of us I was probably the most likely to become a parent – but there's no need to rush off to Mothercare just yet. We were all white, middle aged and middle class. We were all, well, 'normal' I guess. And I was beginning to discover that my normal wasn't theirs.

The point hit home in round 4 of 'The Honesty Game'. You know the rules. Rule 1 – All players must be drunk. Rule 2 – All players must answer all questions honestly. End of rules.

Round 1 was the gentle warm up ... "How many were thinking of changing jobs this year?" Zzzzzzzzzzzzz.

Round 2 was "Which New Year resolutions have been broken already?" Fairly standard mid-January fare.

Round 3 and things were warming up a bit – "When did you first give head?" That was my choice of question. I am pleased to report that I beat Little-Miss-Two-Es by 4 years and 3 months on that one. I smirked, in a non-competitive-but-I-beat-you-bitch way.

No, it was Round 4 when it struck home. And it wasn't even the answer that made the point, it was the question.

"Ok, my turn," giggled Belinda, positively squirming in anticipation. She flicked her hair back over her shoulders for the hundredth time that evening and braced herself for her own question. She took a deep breath.

"How many people around the table have had sex with more than 10 men?"

I waited.

To be honest I was waiting for Belinda to finish her question.

I waited.

And waited.

I looked around the table for guidance. Sophee was

Normal is what you're used to

ready for this one. She couldn't wait to give us the full details. And, not surprisingly, she didn't wait to be invited to talk about herself.

"Well I have slept with 11 men," she boasted.

I raised an eyebrow. She continued, without pausing for breath. If only it could have been a very long speech....

"My first was in 1982. My second, third and fourth were in 1984 in my final year at university," she gushed. "I suppose I went off the rails a bit then."

And that was it. End of answer. That was Little-Miss-Two-E's complete, thoroughly competitive answer.

THAT is when the penny started to drop.

Moreover, there was nothing missing from the question. It really did end with "How many people around the table have had sex with more than 10 men?" For which read "How many people around the table have had sex with more than 10 men, EVER?" Not "How many people around the table have had sex with more than 10 men at the same time / whilst fully trussed up in leather and rubber bondage wear / on a Mediterranean beach at midnight / in the car park behind Tesco's? [delete as applicable], but EVER! Yes 'ever'; 'ever' as in 'in their entire lives'!

I caught sight of the date on the menu – it was that posh a restaurant – 15th January.

There were six people around that table that night. Two of whom had NOT had sex with more than 10 men in their entire lives. One had slept with 'between 10 and 20 men' and two had finally confessed to sleeping with 20-30 men in the last 25 years. Only one had had sex with more than 10 men *so far that year* ...

Ok – so if you compare me with single women of my age than maybe I am not so normal after all. But there again, maybe it was just the company I was keeping. Maybe over time I had simply moved away from the things we used to have in common.

But the following weekend a few more pennies fell. And

Normal is what you're used to

this time I couldn't really blame it on the environment. This time I was on home territory.

The club was filling up nicely. It was about midnight and I was getting into my stride. My eyes weren't yet shut into trance dance mode, and my shirt was still worn. I was in my normal spot, to the side of the dance floor, one step above it. I could see everyone from here, and, more importantly, they could all see me.

A final run through the take-off checklist.

Money? Check.

Pills? Check.

Energy levels? Check.

That'll do. What more do I want?

"Brain to dick, You are cleared for lift-off. Ready to roger, Roger."

The shirt came off. The eyes closed shut. I was ready for orbit. Grinning like a Cheshire Cat on E and mincing away to Kylie I powered away on all cylinders. Thunderbirds are go!

A normal Saturday night for a 39 year old, (oh, ok, 43).

30 minutes into the mission and it was "Houston, we have a problem" time. You know, the line that starts a long adventure with the end always in doubt until the very final minute.

Except in this case the opening line shouted into my ear was "Oi mister – you ever going to bring your legs together?"

I opened my eyes and looked down to see a cute young thing old enough to be the father of my grandchildren, with his hands on my hips and trying to move me aside so he could squeeze by; well, maybe.

How quickly would Little–Miss-Two-E's have responded? Did I care? Maybe she would also have stared at him for 0.01 of a second, decide that those lips needed company and then just get on with it? I don't know. I don't care. I did. And I did.

Communication with others was lost.

Normal is what you're used to

About 20 minutes later, possibly more, possibly less, I opened my eyes to remind myself what this young man looked like. He could certainly kiss and could squirm within my arms very nicely indeed. He had a smooth tum and a smoother bum, with just the right amount of sweat beginning to form and dribble along the middle finger on my left hand. He was washed and ready to go.

"Hmmm," I smiled, pulling my face back to get a proper look. This was the first word I had said to him.

"Yeh, you'll do," he grinned back.

I love it when they play hard to get.

So with the normal gay courtship period over we were ready to move on to the next stage.

But this wasn't to be another normal night of promiscuous sex with a guy half my age. This was going to be a very abnormal night of promiscuous sex with a guy half my age.

We left the club early, not to go home but to go to a house party; and not just any house party, but a 'straight' house party. My newly adopted embryo had been there earlier and had promised to return. I was in the mood for an adventure, and, I have to confess, was more than a little 'straight-curious' to see what they get up to. Well, you read about these wild nights in the Sunday papers and the Monday court reports. Was it true? I wanted to discover the secret twilight world of the hetro-sexual.

But before we could get to the party we had to get a cab ... and that journey allowed another 6 minutes and 36 seconds of tongues. Our tongues. The cab driver seemed to have a problem with this. We didn't. Either that or his brakes were a bit stiff. We were thrown back and forth at every set of traffic lights. Presumably he would have preferred a normal Saturday night ride with one of us chucking up our kebab all over his back seat before we both did a runner without paying the fare. Funny what you get used to isn't it?

We arrived, shaken and stirred. Oh things were

definitely stirring after that 6 minute and 36 second kiss.

"William!" shrieked a boisterous late 20-something over-excited henna-headed waif at the door "You've come back!"

Well, at least I got to know his name.

"I've brought him back with me, is that ok Girl?" He gave me such a dirty grin. He was standing 4 feet away from me, the furthest we had been apart since we met. Fuck! He was cute; very cute indeed.

I was looked up and down by Girl. She didn't like me, that was for sure. The feeling was mutual.

She didn't offer her name and I didn't have time to proffer mine. William had already grabbed me by the hand and was hauling me inside. I shrugged an insincere apologetic shrug as I was dragged inwards. Well, what could I do? William wanted my body and he was definitely going to get it.

We lurched into the house and straight into the bedroom, to deposit our coats of course. But the room was empty and, with a flick of the switch, was dark too. Now, where did I leave those lips ... ?

Needless to say we weren't alone for long. About 2.37 seconds to be accurate before Girl opens the door with "And don't think you are getting up to that sort of stuff on my clean sheets." She smiled indulgently at William before shooting me a look of over-protection.

The door was deliberately wedged open and within a minute the party was sucked into the bedroom with all the girlies rushing up to William to smother him with kisses. He was obviously their favourite, and didn't their beer-gutted boyfriends just know it? They eyed me up. I may be a poof but at least I was would eventually leave with William and free up the girls for them. I had my uses and so they dropped their guard.

I honourably gave him up to the crowd for a few minutes to get the drinks. I fancied a sniff around too, but first there was the urgent matter of the lighting. What kind of

Normal is what you're used to

person has neon strip lights in their bedroom? I am one of the butch-er Brighton boys (ok, so its not saying much, a bit like saying I am one of the butch-er Flamingoes) but even I appreciate a dimmed up-lighter and a few candles. That isn't being camp; that is just being normal.

The music was the same as in the club earlier. The people were of a similar age. The clothes were a bit different – I mean, seriously, who really wears Caribbean flowery shirts with clashing pants other than for a bet? Guess that's breeders for you.

The boys were in the kitchen; the girls were in the corridor; far more rigidly segregated than in the gay club earlier. Was this normal for straights on a Saturday night party; to spend their time avoiding the people they wanted to be with?

I poured myself a plastic pink beaker from the wine box and took a swig.

"Jesus fucking Christ!"

They judge us for what we put into our mouths for fun but what would you prefer? A big thick dick covered in sweet pre-cum or a cup of Tesco's £2.99-a-carton Bulgarian 'bordeaux-esque' vino'. I didn't swallow.

Returning gingerly to the bedroom with two safe bottles of beer, William welcomed me back by hauling and mauling me onto the bed. He was lying in the middle, flecked on all sides with a smattering of chattering girls. On the outer ring of the bedroom were the boys; all touting their testosterone but there were no takers.

William was even more up for this than I was. He dragged me across him and we lay there, respectfully clothed but inseparable. Dropping down onto my elbows, my hands pressing against his cheeks I pushed out my shins to hold his ankles to the bed as I went down for more tongue. He squirmed in mock resistance, and in doing so accidentally kicked one of the trespassing girlies off the bed. Ooops.

And around us they chatted away as though everything

Normal is what you're used to

was normal.

"So how do you think the NHS should be funded?" I kid you not.

But the girls were getting curious now, and, if they were honest, so were the boys. Girl was just getting jealous and several times tried to kidnap my William. He resisted. She insisted. I resisted. She persisted.

"Sorry love, but I've booked his mouth till sunrise."

"Do you mind if I take a photo?" asked a wide-eyed soberly dressed and very badly made-up girl; a little late given that the flash from her Polaroid had already clashed with our retinas via our overly-wide pupils. "Its just that I've never seen two guys kiss each other before."

We stopped and stared at her.

"I ... I ... I just wanted you two to know that I am really comfortable with this," she stumbled.

"Comfortable with what?" I asked.

"Well, you know ..." and she nodded, knowingly, supportively, friendly, welcomingly and very condescendingly.

"Well if you are really that comfortable you wouldn't have mentioned it," I replied. "Indeed, you wouldn't even have noticed it."

And suddenly it dawned on me that she probably wasn't alone. My normality certainly wasn't theirs, nor theirs mine.

Yeh ... its freak show time. I wasn't sure who was in the zoo and who was visiting it, but this was fun. And like a kiddy who throws stones at the lions to hear them roar, it was time to study StraightWorld a bit further, with attitude.

And the girls wanted to know more.

"So William, how does it feel like to be kissed by a man?" one asked.

"Don't you know?" I chuckled, teasingly. "Probably not" would have been a believable answer in her case.

"Oh I didn't mean that, but well, you know ..." She was

struggling and I wasn't going to throw her a lifeline. Why should I? This was fun.

" ... its just different isn't it?"

"Not for me," I replied, and, to prove my point, I got back to it with William.

But she wouldn't take the hint and tapped, no, prodded me on the shoulder. She wanted to know more.

"You two are obviously so in love with each other," she gushed. "Tell me, how long have you been going out together?" She wanted to probe William as much as I did.

William chuckled. The girls leaned forward. The boys went silent. They all wanted to know.

I looked up from William to ask, loudly enough for all the eavesdroppers to hear "What time is it?"

She was baffled. "Erm ... about 3 o-clock I think. Why?"

"In that case ... about 3 hours."

"SHIT!" The boys in the corner were exasperated and their frustration burst out in unison. You could feel them thinking "And they are going to get a fuck tonight. Just look at them. We have to go for weeks before we get the whiff of a whim and they get in after 3 hours. Its just not fair ... blah blah blah."

Oh and this was a red rag to us both. Every moment and every movement from now on was for public display. Even, no, especially, the incident 20 minutes later when, with William pressed against the corner of the bedroom I put my hands down the front of his trousers before milking the pre-cum from his pants, pulling out my hand and pushing my palm across his face for him to lick every drop clean from between my dripping fingers. Oh it was a sweet kiss that followed, made sweeter by the whispered mix of "Oh my God that's disgusting," and "Oh my God that's so fucking horny" from around the room.

Another trip to the kitchen, passing the straight boys by the bedroom door. Oh this was too good an opportunity to miss. I was on a roll.

Normal is what you're used to

With a disarming smile I went over and whispered conspiratorially to them, "Why do dogs lick their balls?"

They looked back, blankly.

I paused, then answered, "Because they can."

Now for the best bit ...

"And why do gay men have so much drug fuelled easy sex?" [pause] ... "Because we can."

The punch-line lived up to its name, winding them deep in the stomach.

Into the packed kitchen for another beer. There, amongst the discarded cans and cartons was an empty small polythene bag, three inches by two. Hmmmm ... that gives me an idea. I looked around and discreetly picked it up.

With the packet in my pocket it was into the bathroom for a rummage amongst the shelves. I just knew I would find what I was looking for there and my instinct was correct. It was now just a matter of timing.

In the bedroom and young William was getting a bit restless; a very encouraging sign. This time he was kneeling on the side of the bed, leaning forward, resting his elbows on the mattress and wiggling around to the music as Girl was trying to lure him away. But he was having none of it.

I approached from behind, gently rubbing up against him, placing my hands proprietarily around his waist. He didn't even bother to look round, he just squirmed some more and pushed back towards my groin. Classy.

Seeing some simulated sodomy simply stimulated Girl into yet another intrusion.

"William," she asked, deliberately excluding me, "Can I ask you a stupid question?"

"Better than anyone I know" I mumbled loud enough for William to choke on his beer.

"Tell me, how do your sort know which one is the man and which one is the woman?"

Well, to be fair to her she did say she was going to ask a stupid question, and she certainly lived up to her

Normal is what you're used to

promise. Not only would this question be stupid at any time but, given that I was bumping and grinding my crotch into William's arse at the time it was also a particularly stupid question.

But the rest waited for the answer.

"Fuck it," I thought, "If they want an answer then I'll give them one."

I looked around the room. They really were keen to know, especially the boys who had turned away, but were craning their heads backwards to hear in their silence.

"Oh there is no point in being gay unless you are going to be versatile," I started, but was met with uncomprehending looks.

"Ok, let me put it this way," I added. William twitched in preparation, but I wasn't meaning him, yet.

"Ok. First of all a question for the girlies." A pause for dramatic effect. "Do you enjoy getting fucked?"

Ok, it was a bit of a direct question, but it was also rhetorical so I moved on quickly.

"And lads," I turned over my shoulder, keeping my hands gripping to William's waist to visually emphasise the point I was making. "Do you enjoy ... [slight pause, then slight thrust] ... fuck-ing?"

They responded with a smirk from an 11 year olds' playground.

I continued.

"And girls, if the boys knew what it felt like to be fucked, do you think they would be better at giving you what you need?" Empowered nods all round.

"And lads, do you think that if the girls knew what it felt like to fuck, do you think that they would be better at taking your dicks?"

I assumed a "yes" reply to both sets of questions....

"Then welcome to our world ... We don't do 'either' or 'or'; we do 'and' and we do 'both'."

A bit too much in their faces? Well, if we had to listen to their questions about our abnormality then they could at least listen to our answers of our normality.

Girl reappeared. She was drunk and plopped onto the bed next to us.

"Phwoarrr!!!! Nice package mate." She grabbed firmly between my legs.

Well this certainly turned the tables. What the fuck was going on here?

I looked at her hand, watching in fear as she started to squeeze. Talk about having me in the palm of her hand ...

"Excuse me, dear, but I think this belongs to you" was all I could think of as I took her right hand in mine and left it right back in her left one.

"How you would have felt if I had grabbed between your legs and said 'nice cunt, lass'."

Yeh, ok – as if I would know the difference between a nice one and a nasty one, but hey-ho, you get the point ...

"It wouldn't be normal for a man to do it to you," I continued calmly "and it certainly isn't normal for a woman to do it to me."

She wafted me away.

Finally, William was ready to move on.

"So Girl, what do you think of him?" William nodded in my direction as we started to put on our coats.

Girl gave me a passing, withering stare and sighed, dryly "William, I think you are being processed."

Not bad, Girl, not bad at all. I must remember to use that line myself one day. But she was too bitter to spot my appreciation.

"Come on you," I patted William's bum, "lets take this party private."

I gently turned him round so we faced the straight boys who perked up when they saw I was ready to take their main threat home.

"Have you got anything to keep us going?" I stage-whispered to William.

"Oh I have a couple of pills left, ... you?"

Cue my moment of triumph ... I grunted as, with an

Normal is what you're used to

exaggerated shove, I pushed my right hand deep into my tight and full jean pocket, pulling out some notes, cigarettes and, oh yeh, a small polythene bag packed to the seams with about 10 grams of white powder.

"Its ok, I have some Charlie, that should keep us going," I whispered. I knew it had been spotted. From the corner of my eye I could feel the nudging of shoulders and the dropping of jaws.

"Come on babes, lets go," I urged.

William paused to pee in the bushes outside the door.

Girl was hovering by the door. She wasn't happy. She was simmering with resentment as I took William away from her. You could see why strangers took an instant dislike to her – it saved time.

As I said my polite goodbyes she took me aside.

"Oh cut the crap," she spat at me "and drop the attitude. Being gay doesn't make you special you know?"

It had never crossed my mind that it did. I didn't consider myself as special, just normal. And lucky.

She hadn't finished yet though.

"I want you to know that loads of my friends are gay," she hissed.

"And I want you to know," I responded, inaccurately but effectively, "that none of my friends are straight. So FUCK OFF!'

"The problem with you is that you are just a rigid dick."

"And the problem with you is that you are just a frigid twat."

Two – nil I think.

I wandered a few steps away and watched William from behind as his stream of hissing pissing fizzled out.

Behind me three of the straight lads appeared. I knew what they were after.

"Scuse mate" said the first. "Can we buy a few lines off you?"

Like lambs to the slaughter. Oh bless ...

With my coyest of looks I struggled one more time to

Normal is what you're used to

pull the bag of powder from my pocket. Holding it in the palm of my hand for all to see I noticed that some grains had splattered onto my hand. With a dab of my wetted left index finger I cleaned that up and fed it to William in front of them all.

Now here was the dilemma. Did I sell them lines of talcum powder from their bathroom at £10 a go, or should I go for the real ball-cruncher instead. Well, be honest, what would you have done?

I decided on the latter.

"Sorry lads," I looked as genuinely apologetic as possible – yeh, like I was sorry! Ha ha ha! – "but this is all I have and … well … we're going to need this ourselves."

Before adding, cruelly, "Actually, I was hoping you might have some spare yourselves that you could have sold us."

They shuffled away back inside. All except the small good looking one. He wasn't giving in that easily. He loitered as William zipped himself. We both looked at him and smiled. We started to walk away.

One … two … three … four …

" 'Scuse me lads" he was there at our shoulders, on cue. I think he was more interested in the coke than the poke but you have to hand it to him, he was trying. Alternatively it was getting late and he had lucked-out on the chance of a fuck with the girls and, well, any port in a storm … What's the difference between a straight boy and a bi-boy at 4am on a Sunday morning? A line of talcum powder.

"Tell me," he asked, talking to my chest, enticing me to lean forward to hear him, "Do you think I should take my shirt off when I dance?" He fingered past the undone top button and rimmed the second one.

As subtlety goes, this wasn't.

I looked over his shoulder at William, who popped a finger into his mouth and imitated a silent retch.

"Oh I think you should do what you feel comfortable with, whatever feels right for you at this moment," I replied.

Normal is what you're used to

"You are only this way once, don't miss the opportunity to live a little."

It was just so obvious.

"So you think I should get it off." He looked from me, to William, to me.

"Do you want to get it off?" I started to prod him.

"I have never got it off with lads at a party before. Maybe tonight could be my first time."

"Do whatever you think is right mate," I whispered, leaning forward, my lips practically tickling his left ear. "But personally I would prefer if you kept it on."

He he he.

"Come on you, lets go." and I pushed William away into the night air.

Another cab ride, another drink and, finally, it was time for the sex. We had done the dancing. We had done the kissing. We had done the teasing. Now it was time for the physical.

I rolled the spliffs as William took a shower and reflected on how normal a night this was to me, but how abnormal it would it have been to them. I wondered how this stage of the evening would develop in StraightWorld. What would have been normal for them?

Would anything have happened on a first night?

Would the evening have climaxed with a peck on the cheek and the promise of being allowed to spend £100 on dinner in a week's time for the prospect of a swap of tongues, but with no guarantee?

Would this have been the stage where, in StraightWorld, we would have chatted for ages, sharing intimate memories from our pasts, gently exploring and getting to know each other? Would we have played each other our favourite music and talked of the last time we cried? Would William have told me of his childhood from the other end of the sofa; avoiding eye-contact and speaking to his teddy bear clasped onto his knees? Would we have shared our dreams for the future. Was this their normal?

Normal is what you're used to

William came from the shower, still dripping slightly, his fair hair tousled and unkempt.

He took his toke before lifting my chin and stared deep into my eyes. He took my hand and led me slowly but purposefully to the bed.

We were now ready for our intimacy. For that precious time where two bodies become entwined as one; giving, taking and sharing the pleasure of each other.

He put a hand to my chest just before the bed, and smiled the sweetest of smiles. He stepped back a step; we looked each other up and then we looked each other down. He was beautiful. I was beautiful. We were beautiful. This was beautiful.

"I think we are ready now, don't you," said William

I agreed with a smile.

"You positive?"

"Oh I have never been more certain of anything."

He turned, allowing the soft, damp amber towel to fall to his ankles. He climbed onto the bed, kneeling away from me. He puts his hands to his bum and gently but purposefully pushed his cheeks apart.

Then, with the magic words "THIS BITCH NEEDS FEEDING!" we *fucked* till lunchtime.

So, am I 'normal'?

What is 'normal'? Well let's have a look at a dictionary definition.

'According to rule'? ... hmmm. Whose rules? I am certainly very normal according to my rules.

'Not deviating from the standard'? – NOT a deviant? Me?!!! How dare you? I'll sue.

'Ordinary'? – I hope not, but then, sometimes, it would be nice.

'Well adjusted'? – I think so, but others disagree.

'Functioning regularly' ... yeh, I function as regular as clockwork mate!

'Having an unbranched chain of carbon atoms'???? –

Normal is what you're used to

I kid you not, look it up for yourself.

'(of a solution) having one-gram equivalent of dissolved substance to a litre'? - Why the litre? Why dilute a gram? Unless, of course, you are going to do that thing with injections up the bum.

'(geometry) a perpendicular'? — At right-angles to everything else? That sounds about right to me.

So when did my normality drift away from a normal normality? Was it ever there in the first place?

Was it normal for boys in north-eastern comprehensive schools to dream wet-dreams of other boys in north-eastern comprehensive schools? Well, it was certainly normal for me and for most of the girls in north-eastern comprehensive schools to dream wet-dreams of boys in north-eastern comprehensive schools.

Is it normally normal to have so much sex with so many different people? Or is that normally a fantasy and not normally a reality.

Is it normal for a 43 year old to mince away to Kylie?

Well it is certainly normal for me.

Oh I could find reasons and stories as to why I was different and alienated when I grew up; but whilst I could make a heart-rending story it wouldn't really be my reality. The truth is that I was never really excluded from anything, other than by my own choice. Or 'taste' as I prefer to call it.

But I never moved away at right-angles from the rest of society by stopping to be attracted to girls. I never started in the first place. It was no parting of the ways; no deviation from my normal.

Have I suffered from prejudice? Not really, well, not then. Announcing "I am a poof" gets a positive reaction these days from strangers, but you try saying "I am a positive poof" and see what happens to your friends. This is also my normal.

Normal is what you're used to

University came and went; nephews and nieces appeared all over the place.

At work colleagues bring pictures of kids who all look the same. When they start to worry about school fees and nannies is when they drift away from my normal. Their normal is baby-sitters and baby-shitters.

Mine isn't.

But my normal has included watching my friends die.

My normal has included my address book with pages, yes whole fucking pages, ripped out. Obsolete.

In my 20s my normal was black ties and funerals; theirs was champagne and christenings.

My normal is of a life expectancy that I have already exceeded.

My normal has gifted me today; and gifted me the gift of realising that today really is a gift.

My normal includes my 3 daily pills and 3 monthly tests; my anxious days and my night sweats.

This is my normal, and normal is what you are used to.

Others' normal includes walking everywhere with a well-trained Labrador, or thrice weekly trips for dialysis, or a life in a wheel chair.

That is their normal, this is mine, what is yours?

That is why "I am a normal guy. I am the same as everyone else. I just happen to be gay" is such bollocks.

No-one is normal. We are all equal, but none are the same.

Get used to it.

27

A paean to HIV

RV

Hello, HIV, how's your life
And where are you going?

Call me if you need me
And let's be buddies, let's be mates

O, HIV, I love you
O, HIV, I love you
I'm always thinking of you

You've taught me so much
And I'm glad to have known you
But it's time to move on and let go

O, HIV, I love you
O, HIV, I love you
Will no one rid me of you?

At times, you've made me feel so alone, so afraid
But you've given me the chance to change, to grow
And now I want you to go

O, HIV, I love you
O, HIV, I love you
I know who you are now

You've always been the 'but' in my life
But now, I have a future
And I'll live in tomorrow

O, HIV, I love you
O, HIV, I love you
I now know where you're hiding

A paean to HIV

You know, if I die, then you die too
So let go your hold on me
And let's grow old together

O, HIV, I love you
O, HIV, I love you
I have the measure of you now

You've known all along
That I'm the one in control
And I'll always win in the end

O, HIV, I love you
O, HIV, I love you
I'm always thinking of you

So, HIV, you'd better watch out
Cos I now know what you're about
And I'll seek you out and I'll get you ...

28

Reflections of the past

William

January 1984 was not a good year for me. This was the year I was told that I was HIV positive. Since that year my life changed.

During the first six weeks of being told that I was HIV, it was terrible. Newspapers full of headlines like 'Gay plague', 'It's their own fault', 'You can catch it by kissing'. I really thought I would be six feet under within a week.

At the timel had just a few of close friends that I could turn to. Without their support and kindness, I am not sure what would have happened.

I had no counselling after my diagnosis, so I got myself re-tested thinking it was just a bad dream. But no, the test still said that I was positive.

I eventually got to grips with myself and determined that *life must go on.* I could not let this get to me. As I had no symptoms and was not ill, I went straight back to work; just got on with things.

It was only if I met a anyone I got a bit scared. I did not want to get too close to anyone. My mind was ruling my body. I was just scared of passing anything on to anyone. It was best if I just kept myself to myself.

But it did not work out like that.

I met this guy who I really liked. I had just ended a six-year relationship, which knocked me for six, so the last thing on my mind was getting into another relationship.

At the beginning he knew nothing of my status. One evening he asked, "Are you ok?"

I replied, "Yes."

Then I could not hold back, saying "There was something I needed to tell you."

Reflections of the past

I had dreaded this moment. He looked a bit worried so I said, "I am HIV positive."

He replied, "It will be ok. There is nothing to worry about. We will get through." He thought that I was about to chuck him.

A few tears were shed that night.

We are still together. We will be celebrating ten years together in February 2003.

When I look back to the early days of taking my drugs, then just a few tablets, I was told that for the first two weeks of starting the drugs I would feel lousy with side effects kicking in and being sick.

Whenever it happened, my partner was there, ready to clear it up. It takes a strong stomach to deal with that sort of thing. How long was this to go on, I asked myself.

It lasted about a month and eventually things quietened down.

I felt really lucky having to be able to have these drugs as many of my best friends were not so lucky. They did not have the combination drugs around the time of their diagnosis.

I always remember my dearest departed friends if I go to any social events, wishing they were there too, to enjoy the evenings.

I started my present treatment in 1992 when my life took another turn. The drugs now rule me. I now take my tablets at the same time each day and night, regardless of where I might be, even If I go to the theatre. This is a real pain and can't be missed.

Skin rashes, chest infections, mouth ulcers, weight gain then weight loss. I am diabetic too, so I have to take insulin. Having to stick a needle into yourself is not easy. Six years on and I still cannot get used to it.

Having spent some time in and out of hospital over the past years I can hold my head up and say, "Yes, I am still here!"

I am lucky to be here. I think the reason for this is the

way I have been able to deal with this virus, by not letting it get to me, not sitting about worrying.

I cannot do anything to turn the clock back, so I plan ahead. I have a purpose: to live my life and enjoy it while I can. Yes I have my ups and downs as we all do at times in our lives.

I have a really supportive partner and many good close friends – what more could I ask for? A cure would be nice. I think that is not too far away to become reality.

I hope these words might be of some comfort to anyone who has just been diagnosed with HIV.

Always remember you are not alone.

World Aids Day 2002

29

Return to sender

Richard Thomas

Clean your teeth
Wash your hair
Mind those who watch and stare
Looking to you
Looking for reason
To play into you
Absolute treason

They're the ones
To do you damage
No fault of their own
For they are damaged
Contradictions in terms of war
Play them safe
No more no more
Why do they hurt us?
Why attack
The name of the game
Give back give back

Try it once
You'll feel my attack
I'll crucify you
Get back get back

Grind me to pulp
You know me not
Mind yourself
Hold back hold back
Only ignorance do you bestow

Return to sender

Your vileness is deceit I know
Upon my breast you rested your head
This is what you should know instead

I am a carnivore
Concede retreat
Give up false victory
You are no meat
Else wise to hell
Will you derive?
And your conscience
Will be mine

Believe me this
Believe it true
Because I now see
Straight through you
Right into that heart of yours
Which from beginnings was untoward
So learn your lesson
And learn it well
I pierce your good heart so well
How painful does this feel for you?
My goodness dear
How true, how true

So sorry it hurts
This scathing attack
As once I said
"Give back, give back"

Goodbye you now and
Fair ye well
Oh bastard you
Learn well learn well.

30

The ribbon song

Mike Nelson

I want to reach out my hand and touch you
In a Way you'll understand
With my fingertips gently burning
with countless tactile sensations
that only your skin will feel

I want to open my lips to you like a rose
and speak to you
In a voice whose language
only you can hear and understand.

I want to weave a part of me
into the beating of your heart
and the rushing of your mind.
Using softly whispered songs of hopes and dreams,
do feel the same about me?

Our spirits through the light of HIV
seem to share a mutual knowledge,
a shared understanding I'm sure at times
run as one like a soft silken thread
through our hearts and minds

And when I look into your eyes,
I see hope, a way forward, a brand new horizon
For already you can draw my emotions from me
like a scarlet ribbon

To tie around your arm, a kind of badge,
a symbol from me to you

The ribbon song

A silent band of strength that
I hope no one will ever be able to break

The mask of repeated history and all its chains
crack a little more each time I am in your arms.
I hope it won't be long before
it breaks and falls away,
so that I can reveal my whole self to you,

And all the love I know that I can give you
can let flow my full potential
So that I can share
the joy of total freedom and hope with you.

*Dedicated to all those who love in
the face of adversity and suffering*

31

Of sacrilege and sodomy

Oliver Speer

Sometimes some wise and woeful words
Can ring true through the turgid dirge
Life's lukewarm mediocrity
Uplifted to lucidity
Words heard when only two or three
Can redefine one's destiny
To deviate well-trodden paths
Now furrowed deep from all the years
Of stale tradition and routine

As once my mother said to me
When I was only two or three
To live your life and always be
– Yourself, and above all things, free
But one thing you must learn, she'd say
That there will be a price to pay
For those who walk tradition's halls
To smash the archives of routine
And shamelessly to vent their spleen

So if my life's a littered spree
Of sacrilege and sodomy
Demoralised morality
These sisters to my sanity
If all to me is shit and hate
All life's virtues, I desecrate
Debase, debauched, degenerate
This canker I precipitate
If I should die, and die diseased
Then please think only this of me
That I have lived my life for me
I was, and ever will be free.

32

Just a dream

Oliver Speer

Go back to sleep, it's just a dream,
Toothless, torn from mother's breast
And smashed against the cold concrete,
It's just a dream, go back to sleep.

Go back to sleep, it's just a dream,
The words that every mother said
When wracked and writhing in your bed
And torn apart at every seam,
Go back to sleep, it's just a dream

Go back to sleep, it's just a dream,
I wake choked with a cotton breath
My mouth stuck shut with gum of flesh
And nothing remains as it seeemed,
Go back to sleep, it's just a dream

Go back to sleep, it's just a dream,
My ma once uttered by my bed.
Cut with my fingernails, my head
She'd heal my wounds and help me keep
My sanity ... go back to sleep.

33

Sanctuary

Andrew Hanuman

I took great care in preparing my new home. Meticulously laying flat the long grasses, thoughtfully and with love I created this sanctuary. The sounds of war were now too far away to be heared. The terrible screams of the injured had become too familiar. The tragic cries of the dying had made me wish for deafness. Everyone died alone in this war, obsessing on wrong doings, justifying their hatred and bitterness that they would not escape from.

Forgiveness was an illusive stranger.

I decided that to be a deserter in this war was the rational and only thing to do. I just did not understand the war and viewed both sides in this brutal conflict as misguided, selfish and cruel. I took no sides and for that, I was punished, sent to the front line armed with killing machines and blades of steel. To inflict pain and death on the enemies. Knowing no other way of existence I stopped questioning the cruelty and madness of this world and believed infact it was me who was mad for being so different from everyone that that I'd ever met.

In my hand, I held close the small statue of the beautiful Nun, her kind and caring face smiled lovingly. Her arms were held out as if inviting me to run to them, perfect love from the perfect mother. She intoxicated me.

With enough food to last a week. a warm blanket and plenty to drink. I would be able to lie low for a few days and then go to the Dock and smuggle myself out on a cargo ship. It did not matter where but there had to be something different to this. Running away could be viewed as being cowardly but I saw it as survival.

My new home resembled a crop circle, perfectly formed,

Sanctuary

although not formed by aliens, it was spectacular to me. In this tempory space, I would have time to rest .After making it out alive of the last bloody battle; I was worn out, exhausted and about to fall apart. I needed respite from the hatred. I wanted quiet.

I loved it when both the sun and the moon were in the sky at the same time, it looked magical. I lay in my new home and watched the faces and shapes appear in the clouds above. I did not see the images of war but saw childlike figures drifting above me. Clowns beamed, while dolphins elegantly dived in and out of the white fluff. Cats chased dogs frantically while sailboats went by gracefully. I was safe at last.

I was woken by the sound of my name being called, I froze, they new I was here I thought. But how could they, my puzzled mind shifted focus to the fear of capture. I new I would be punished by whoever was seeking me. Would I be killed for daring this escape, I looked at the statue and prayed.

I managed to control my breathing but my heart refused to participate in this survival game. Almost pushing its way out of my chest, like a crazed cage animal desperate for escape. I wanted to scream out, end this madness. If peace could only be achieved by death, then so be it.

They did not realise when they looked down at the small five year old that it wasn't a play pen I had created. It was my sanctuary.

I didn't say anything as I was picked by the family friend, I didn't cry. Like any prisoner of war I held my head high and looked straight ahead, towards my place of incarceration and torture.

My mother opened the door, her eyes full of tears she grabbed me to her and held me as if I was so precious, I snuggled into her chest and almost felt safe. My father pulled up in his car, I panicked and started crying, I then panicked about crying." I'll give you something to cry about if you don't shut up." He would say.

Sanctuary

He thanked the man for finding me while he gave me a look of incomprehension. The man told them that he found me making a playpen in the park and that Id been playing with a nun doll. My father quickly jumped in. "it's not a bloody doll" he said" he's very religious, going to Sunday school, that's all "I was told to go to my room and wait. My father looked embarrassed and glared at my mother.

I knew my punishment was to come, a torturous game was played. Would I be left for hours or would I hear the shouts of fury coming towards me in my next breath. I could here shouts coming from downstairs. I could here my mothers insults and my fathers retaliation, they did not care about themselves, how could I expect them to take care of me. I had experienced something today that they could never take from me – peace. I had found a safe place, created by me, for me. I knew then and there, in that special moment, that if I was to survive this awful war I must find sanctuary whenever possible. I had found hope that day!

The nurse came in and interrupted my sleep. "How you feeling, love" she asked in her usual buttery manner. "yeah fine, was just dozing," my voice slurred from the Pethadine. "Need to steal some blood from you sweetheart" she said apologetically. "you're a bit sweaty, shall I check your temperature?"

"Mind if you don't" I asked, "can you leave me for a bit, just had a bit of a strange dream that's all, feel a bit freaky." "Ooh you on the Efavirenze then" she asked excitedly like I was a participant in some new underground designer drug culture. Acid house this isn't I thought. "No used it for a while but it wasn't exactly conducive with my fragile mental health " laughing and slurring at the same time which produced a sound like a baby seal about to be clubbed to death. " No problem, I'll come back after lunch and do them then, anything you want just ask, ok " Her voice reassuring as ever. She left me in the comfort of my little room.

One of the advantages of being positive is that due to stigma and discrimination it is often the case that if possible

Sanctuary

hospital stays are bettered by having privacy of a single room or at least space to create a little den on an open ward with the curtains.   I start to feel guilty that this pleasure is not afforded to all NHS patients but hey I often have to hide my illness from others in order to protect myself from prejudice. Most people don't.

I think back to my dream, ok my childhood memory of when I created a safe place. I wonder why I am remembering this now. Is it because I feel safe perhaps? Is it because I feel cared for? Or is it because I'm scared as hell?

I'm an adult now and still caught up in a war. Except this is a very different war, and the battles are being raged inside me. Yet I have my Cavalry at my side, the pills and potions are my nuclear arsenal and my consultant is my President Bush, fixated on wiping out the enemy. Yes I do feel cared for. Yes I feel safe. Here in the sanctuary of my hospital bed ...

34

Poem after Rimbaud

Oliver Speer

Oiled as the wetness of a womb
All pebble-dashed upon the drum
My silence echoes round the room
The copper taste of salt and cum

Into the gasping burrow delves
The ferret as each piston-pump
Rattles the railings of the shelves
Causing my kidneys twist and jump

Oh tear my body limb from limb
Make a sweet pudding of my brain
And sew fine garments of my skin
To cover up your naked shame

Now cure me of this donkey's lust
With every thrust attest my sin
I put my colon to your trust
And feel the ferret wet within

35

Septic Leg

Oliver Speer

Oh, sing me a song
Of your soul's sweet salvation

Don't dig yourself deeper
In dark degradation

Don't lie there and languish
In leper's repose
With an arse for a mouth
And a cock for a nose
And two clitoral ears
And a festering fist

As your pinpoint eyes weep
Like the pus from a cyst

And all of the things
You should never have caught
Like the herpes and scabies
And genital warts
And the crabs in your pubes
And your legions of lice
You're scratching it raw now

But isn't it nice?
As the skin flakes away
And you wank yourself red

I've kept a space warm for you
Come back to bed

36

So ...

Emmanuel Lalopoulos

He came from the sea,
Or so he said.

He asked for a kiss
And I gave him a kiss
A kiss of life

I dried him with my shirt
He was one handsome man

He came back with me
And stayed with me
For a time

I felt the hardship of his skin
When I took him in my arms
And when I looked in his eyes
I saw the depths of the sea

He slept next to me
Woke up next to me
And so it would finish all well
But this is no fairy tale

So you can't ask
For a seaman to deny the sea,
Or so he said ...

But one day
The sky sank into the sea
My seaman was gone ...

37

The sounds of summer

Mike Nelson

The tide rolling gently in to play at our feet
As hand-in-hand we walk along the shore

The cry of gulls flying into the sunset
And the soft crack of pebbles beneath our feet
The gentle song of the breeze that ruffles our hair
And whispers into our hearts
whose beats resound in our ears

The call of our emotions
from somewhere deep within
Playing the sweet music
of the words of love you speak to me

All these precious sounds
will soon be memories
Locked with fondness into our dreams
For they are the sounds of summer
One so special
because you are here walking with me

38

A stench I cannot forget

a pretty boy

A foul stench
A mixture of mothballs and shit
Breathing over my shoulder
It wispers in my ear
Of rotten teeth and incense
A pretty boy, my curse
Would it happen had I been ugly?

My catholic school uniform
With grey shorts
A gentle stroke, he's so gentle
A hand slips inside
He's trying to be nice
I'm on his knee
As he wispers to me

Holy pictures on the wall
The colour purple in them all
Jesus on a cross, he looks so sad

I must face the wall is what he said
In his room, an iron bed
I wish he would finish,
The stench always there
I'm only eight, why am I here?

..But I was.

Thirty five years later
I still hate the colour purple
And the smell of mothballs

39

Still waters

Mike Nelson

Pull me into the water with you
hold me so close
that my body melts into yours

Wipe the tears from my eyes
and take their scars away
with your gentle fingertips

Wash all the pain away
cleanse me with the soothing touch
of your sweet caress

Heal all the wounds from my past
that far too long have refused to let go
Wash away their memories
and banish their ghosts

Your hands across my breast,
take the chill from my heart
and sets it beating again

Set my lips aflame with your kiss
infuse them with passion once again
Teach me to speak only your names
as these still waters run deep
as you make love to me

Put back together
all of the scattered pieces
of my broken dreams

Still waters

Fill out the hollow chamber that is my soul
with the radiant sounds of your laughter

Flood my views
with the rushing tide of your love
I feel it rippling beneath the surface of my skin
that far too long was bleached out
by fear and isolation

But now I am here
in these waters with you
lost in the cascading emotions
that flow over me

I have a new reason to carry on
to live only to be with you.

40

Survivor

Jude

1997

Each morning I woke, looking foreword to the day ahead and WHAM: a big black cloud bursts all over, full of HIV and Hep C and all that would change my life.

When I got the result, for the first time in my life, I cried unashamedly in very public places. The train ride home was a blur; so many thoughts, anxieties and problems; my head was full.

Later that day I went for a walk on the beach. My younger son was surfing, so contented and absorbed. We waved and shouted hello, I smiling to hide the shock, he smiling his beautiful smile back.

How to tell my two sons, grown-up men, too intelligent to lie to; and if I did, when would I stop? How did they feel then? Shocked? Sad and upset? But always supportive?

How do they feel now? Well, we don't talk about it a great deal. It's not that its unimportant but simply that I can't quite get my head around my health status, and anything about them in the same sentence. I cannot even write about it in letters. My answer to their question of how I am is usually "fine" – the universal stock reply.

1999

Surprisingly life carried on more or less as usual except in my head there seemed so much to worry about. Like the future: was there one and how to cope. Money, housing and keeping healthy, when would Aids become part of my life. Not even if but when. So I continued working as a night sister getting odd infections, having biopsies: the usual stuff. Energy was in short supply. It was work, rest and sleep – lots of sleep.

After three years my ill-health forced me to retire. I grieved so much for a long, happy and rewarding career. After a few months sulking I began to look ahead, went to evening classes and looked towards a goal.

The same year a phone call invited me to take on a very badly treated old cat. Not only was she scabby, frightened and very sorry for herself, she was angry with a capital A. It took three years to hug her into a still timid but gentle loving sweetheart. We have helped to heal each others hurt. I can tell her all my fears and who is she going to tell! Two old girls together.

2002

As it does, life has moved on – I am 17 months into a degree course and have just started combination therapy (something I said I would never do). My tutors know about my health status and are more than supportive. My marks do not send rockets into orbit but I pass, so far. Most of all I want to live and love it.

Next year all things being equal, three of us from uni, all over fifty, are walking the London marathon, not running you note. If you spot us, one looking particularly knackered, it will be me. Grinning from ear to ear proving that anything is possible.

There have been many hurdles, rivers of tears, and no doubt, more to come. I am certainly more emotional and still worry about money, secure housing and sometimes about people finding out and judging me. Hey, do I care? Well, actually I do – I have the humility to think "there for the grace of God … " Many people encourage and enable me; they give me courage and often a big hug too. Sometimes the virus makes me feel dirty and unclean, at other times shiny and fine.

Survivor

If you pass an open window and hear "you must have been a beautiful kitten" sang out of tune to a totally bemused but happy cat, well you know who it is – so join in!

May 2003

Hey, it's nearly 'high' summer again, and so much has happened since my last reflections in this book. The cat is still very hairy, very sleepy and loving. I have moved into long-term accomodation. Relief. No worries about six month lease reviews. And if you are on benefits, asking your son to be a guarantor. Humbling stuff! Very!

Two types of combination therapy have been tried and rejected. Many unexpected side effects. And what they do to your head! It is of no comfort to think that they may prolong your life when in fact that life has become a misery of nausea, diarrhoea, body changes and the most alarming nightmares and screaming. Very off-putting and frightening to any weekend visitor.

Highlight in March was a trip to New Zealand to see my younger surfer son. He sent the ticket and with a very small rucksack, little energy reserves, but lots of anticipation, off I went. He took it at my pace, and though seeing me with a great difference in lack of energy and weight loss, we saw and enjoyed so much beauty and sorted out some issues.

The tears when I left him ...

This HIV has made me realise that due to the distance and finance we simply will not meet again. Yet I remain happy and optimistic all the time, a fact that some people find quite difficult. A member of my family, looking at photographs of a night out with other positive people remarked, "But you look so happy." My response is unprintable but along the lines of "and why not?" Almost all of the positive people I have met just do not fit the stereotype that has been potrayed out there. So anyone reading this and feeling smug, beware: it is silent and it looks totally normal.

Survivor

Its Uni holidays soon and unbelievably they have not sussed me out yet and thrown me off the course. It has been hard work but so stimulating. In October it is final year and I believe that it, and the arrival of a great niece have kept me going. New life and new possibilities for a better informed, educated, aware and healthy generation. So here's to you Sofia (my niece), bottoms up (well it usually is at six months) for an exciting life.

41

These things

a host

These things
Introduced to me
Unwanted, enter me

These things
Looking for a battle ground
Ready for war
Found it

Perfect
Battle proceed
Millions of troops — the reds

Will they succeed?
Perhaps

No! Say the whites
This is our ground
We will kill these things
Wherever they are found
Multiply! Multiply!
say the whites
We've got to get them out of his life

COME ON YOU WHITES
The reds taking over
wherever they will

Got ya ...
Making you ill,
these things

Two years later
Not feeling so ill
The whites take over
With the help of the pills

Victory, maybe
These things latest score:
CD4 whites, 480
Virus reds, 50

42

Victim

a pretty boy

So many infected not knowing at all
When will they realise when they will fall
So many others
So many times

Twenty new cities
And what do I find ...
It carries on

Some of us had no choice
Some of them did
Some are ignorant
Was it Tom, Dick, Harry
or was it Sid

Some are raped, brutally or date
Some carry on
Some of them don't
Some for revenge
Some don't care

Beware!
Beware he's out there
So be cautious, wherever you are

He may be beautiful
Nice body, flash car
He is out there
Never too far

So many others
So many times
Soon it will be you

Victim

Don't talk of heartaches
Remember them all
For fuck's sake be careful
One day he'll call

43

Voodoo

Andrew Hanuman

Tim had always been a party animal, one of the first on the dance floor at any club or party and usually the very last to get off.

He liked everything in its place though; his nights compartmentalized into fluorescent little Tupperware containers.

It was too much trying to do everything at once, especially after too much K. He hated cruising on the dance floor, it interfered with his dancing and it stopped him getting into the music. Like a man possessed by a beautiful demon, he would submerge himself into the sounds of the disco. His body as if making passionate love to the bass, while his pleasured mind rode the electronic symphony. He liked the big records, synthesized sounds – computer generated white noise, sexy and almost metallic. Thumping chemical beats, decent songs and clever breaks that gave you just long enough to re-deodorize the dance floor.

He would fill the time between the many clubs he adventured in by stumbling off to one of the many chill-outs. If he were lucky he might secure a drug fuelled long and drawn out session with something horny before continuing his hedonistic adventure. Tim would be waiting patiently in the queue for the next club to open, whatever the weather, as long as he was Chemed up or guaranteed he would be soon. It was his religion, and clubland was his spiritual watering hole. The gods of decadence and pleasure he gratefully worshiped. Danny was often at his side.

Danny passed Tim a bottle of water and said in his strong South Wales accent, "Listen love, if you can imagine that HIV is a train heading for Cardiff, Cardiff symbolizing

Voodoo

AIDS and death. The time the train will arrive will depend on both the speed of the train – your viral load – and the length of track left – your CD4 count – before reaching Cardiff."

Tim had heard some garbled nonsense of drug-speak in his life but this was more than trippy. Danny continued, "What you can do, love, is slow the train down with drugs so that it might never reach Cardiff at all, in fact it might go no further that Bristol Parkway"

"Oh good, drugs, what a wonderful treatmen. Can I choose the cocktail," said Tim giggling. "Trips, E, K and a bag full of Charlie, taken as required."

"Don't know why I bother, you nutter," said Danny irritated.

"C'mon lets dance." Tim grabbed the wasted Danny and they headed for the frenzy of the dance floor. For the next few hours they would bathe in the laser beams, blissed out, fully involved and loving it.

Danny and Tim had been best friends since school. they came from a small seaside town, Barry Island, in Wales. It was a strange place to grow up: very quiet and deserted for half of the year but when Easter came the fairground would open and Barry Island would take on a new identity. Day-trippers with their screaming children would come from all over Wales to chase the thrills of the fun fair, while gorging on chips and gravy, candyfloss and cockles. They would eagerly swim in the polluted sea and do the numerous arcades with its bingo callers and tacky prizes. It had a huge Butlin's camp where Danny and Tim would sneak into and lust after the sexy red-coated men. These were happy times but they also new that they had to leave and head for the bright lights and adventures that Wales could not offer. Aged only 17 they arrived in Brighton.

The years that followed were filled with many ups and probably too many downs, but in the Slime bar this night, they were happy, contented and trashed.

Tim had been diagnosed HIV positive a few months

Voodoo

earlier and the news had hit him for six. He was not terribly shocked but more angry and disappointed in himself; he thought he had been careful but he guessed not careful enough. He refused to beat himself up about it. With his typical optimistic outlook on life he shrugged it all off. Danny had been distraught when Tim told him and had spent all his time since getting information from HIV organizations and the Internet. They were like brothers. This had left Danny feeling helpless, he so wanted to take it away from Tim, and he was angry that he might one day loose his best friend.

"Lets do a k booty bump," said Tim enthusiastically.

"Oh really? In here on the dance floor?" said Danny laughing.

"In the cottage of course," said Tim

"Look," said Danny looking serious for a moment. "We need to talk. Its five in the morning, the clubs nearly empty. Lets go back to yours, have a smoke and chill out for a while."

Tim sat up in his seat. "Why the serious face mister? You starting your comedown early?"

"No, but c'mon lets go," said Danny as he went off to the coat check to get their jackets.

The sun was bright as they left the club; the chemicals consumed that evening turned up the usual colours of autumn. The trees were filled with an array of beautiful reds and gold, shimmering in the early morning sun. The Palace Pier cartoon, like toy town, resembling the fun fair from Disney's Pinocchio. The smell of hot frying donuts and candyfloss wafted over, while the sea danced frantically around, gnawing at its structure. A faint hue of psychedelic purple and green outlined the buildings nearby and the day-tripper's arriving on the street looked like they were made from Plasticine.

Tim looked at Danny and laughed, "We've lost time again haven't we. Let's get a cab quick, the living dead are coming."

Voodoo

Back in the warmth of Tim's flat, they sat and drank warm tea while Tim mixed down tempo tunes on his favourite toy, his mixing decks. Tim was not aware of Danny's eyes upon him. He was entranced by the sounds coming from the speakers, and he loved his mixing and was always happy to perform his superstar DJ thing whatever state he was in.

Danny had learnt much about HIV in the last few months. He had read a lot of clinical stuff, but was also very interested in the concept of how the power of the mind can be harnessed to act as a healer.

HIV is like Voodoo in that being a terminal condition it was assumed it was only a matter of time until sickness and death. Hopelessness and acceptance of fate was like 'pointing the bone at the intended victim'. Danny had come to the conclusion that it was not just combination therapy that was keeping most people well now, but that people now had a sense of hope. If he could get Tim to believe that he had a future then may be he would survive.

He could not watch his friend die; he needed Tim's friendship, and he was desperate for a solution.

"That sounds really lush Tim, why don't you start doing DJ'ing in clubs or sell your mixes? You hate your job, and you would love it."

"Danny, my job's ok. Fancy going to the sauna? That man with the gorgeous tattoo on his back might be there, yum!" said Tim with a sparkle in his drug fucked eyes.

"I think you need to get some sleep soon. Hey, Tim, why don't you get a boyfriend? It has been ages since you finished with arsehole face." Danny was pushing it.

"Do you really think I am that stupid love. I do know what you're up to." He passed Danny the spliff and continued, "Danny I know you care, but you have been weird ever since I found out I have the virus. Just because I am not falling apart that does not mean I am not in pain. I cannot stand all this. You're constantly on one. Danny, I am going to make another cup of tea and while I'm away I want you to think about what I say.".

Voodoo

"Am I doing it all wrong as usual?" asked Danny sheepishly.

"No," said Tim "but your fear is eating you up and you're putting it on me. Fear is the killer. When you look at me don't see a dying man, see a man truly alive. Don't try and change me into someone I don't recognize. I feel strong and I intend to survive. You're my mate, Danny. I love you but don't put your fear on me ... it drains. Chill out babe."

Tim left the smoke-filled dimly lit room to make the tea.

A few minutes later Danny entered the kitchen to witness Tim giggling to himself, dancing with tea towels.

Nearly cracking up with laughter Danny managed to say, "You nutter. Sort yourself out, love, were off to the sauna, and then who knows, the state were going to get into it will be a party with the space men ... "

44

World Aids Day

Mike Nelson

days of red ribbons

We are used to seeing a multitude of coloured ribbons; pink, white, blue and even rainbow; however the original **red ribbon** has become less visible over time.

Why am I telling you this? Well, Sunday 1st December, World AIDS Day, is a day of remembrance for those affected by HIV and AIDS. Its symbol is the once ever present **red ribbon**. Due to a mixture of familiarity and complacency its once trademark huge ribbon banners, remembrance marches and candle-lit vigils have all but disappeared.

The problem of HIV and AIDS has not diminished nor has its effects on people reduced. It is true that modern medicines have given a number of sufferers a chance for respite from its progression, however not all can benefit from these very toxic drugs. Whilst they reduce the number of people dying from AIDS, these same people now suffering are dying from the side effects of prolonged toxic drug regimes.

absolute regimes + malfunctioning systems

Part of the problem lies in the need for absolute adherence to medication regimes. Unlike any other medical condition, taking just a few doses late, with the wrong food or missing them places the sufferer at real risk of becoming resistant to the beneficial effects of the medication.

Many sufferers, although looking relatively well compared to those of a few years ago, still suffer from severe fatigue, nausea, incontinence, loss of sensation in fingers and toes, liver and kidney damage, light sensitivity, arthritis, painful movement, osteoporosis and body fat distribution leaving 'beer belly' type stomachs with gaunt faces. Little wonder many people lock themselves away from the general public.

Social in-Security, social housing-less

The situation is made worse as the Social Security system now no longer sees the disease as a severe life threatening condition (despite it still being so) and sufferers who are disabled by its affects are now unable to get full access to the help and benefits they need to survive whilst other less severe conditions are given automatic access to these benefits.

In Brighton the problems are particularly bad. Although the local medical services are much better than the average, those who need to stay in the area to gain access to such services are finding the local housing crisis a particular problem. And those in private accommodation are priced out. There is no social housing available for those with medical needs. This makes an interesting comparison with sheltered retirement accommodation: there is actually a surplus but reserved for those over retirement age only.

less Red Ribbon-ers = less visibility

As the original campaigners and champions of those affected by this disease have disappeared slowly (for this read died) very few have taken up their cause as it is rare for someone not affected to try and overcome the strong prejudice against those affected by it. For this reason, the visibility of people affected by this disease has reduced as it is still associated with the disenfranchised, and labelled 'high risk groups'.

human, alive, and at risk

A very worrying trend is shown in recent figures: the problem is still expanding outside its traditional 'closed' groups and an increasing number of the 'mainstream' (mainly heterosexual young women) are being infected, the very people that due to prejudice and ignorance believe incorrectly that they are not at risk from this disease. The truth is that if you are human and alive then you are at risk.

ignorance – the contagious prejudice

The problem comes from people's inability to talk about this problem openly as there is still a stigmatisation. A sufferer who informs people that their medication is 'oral chemotherapy' in order to avoid negative reactions from others, after being told to leave a restaurant when asking for a glass of water to take their HIV medication! Part of the reason for this abominable behaviour is people's ignorance and fear, despite the disease not being contagious (it can only be passed on through internal exchange of body fluids) people still have irrational fears and prejudice against those affected.

informed awareness

So please think of those affected by this terrible and incurable condition on the 1st December and wear a red ribbon and try to bring awareness of this back into the attention of the public.

45

Pseudo masochism?

Oliver Speer

An account of a dream

I am at home, expecting no one, I hear a knock on the door and open it to see an old vague friend. His nondescript face seems to be an amalgam of all the characters who exist on the borders of my social past, present and future existence and I can tell from his expression that he knows me better than I know him.

With an embarrassed and nervous tone to his voice and movements, he tells me he came to confide in me.

"Something's been upsetting me and I thought you would be the only person who might understand," he says, looking at me with his head hung low in painful shame.

"The thing is ... " he pauses and takes a deep breath as if his words will require great strength to force out, " ... I have a tendency to be an extremely sadistic and masochistic person."

With a brave face and a sense of relief from the burden of his long burning secret, he looks at me straight in the eye hoping for some glimmer of recognition, something more than empathy, a deeper understanding. I look at him back and smile sympathetically, I reach out my arms to comfort him, "It's okay," I say "I don't have a problem with that, ... it's not uncommon."

As I embrace him I am unaware that he is reaching into his pocket to retrieve something. I feel a movement slice across my face, my arm, my leg, followed by a high-pitched stinging pain and look to see great white chunks of surface flesh fall from my body, cut with a razor-sharp metal object not unlike a cheese grater.

I am horrified and swiftly back away, gawking in stunned

silence. He lunges toward me and despite the agony of my fresh wounds, I fight with all my strength to prevent him from tearing me apart with nails, teeth and whatever else is at hand. In a desperate attempt to try and stop him I grip his head in both hands and with my thumbs I push his eyeballs deep into their sockets. He just grins manically and with insane vigour, strips away at the skin of my back with his fingernails. I try to crush his windpipe; he is gnawing away at my right cheek with relish. I attempt to knee him in the balls but somehow miss; there seems to be no way to stop him.

I am growing weaker, loosing blood (by now through some means or another we both seem to be naked). He has somehow acquired a kitchen knife, maybe a reincarnation of his previous weapon; it is just as sharp, with ease it severs three of my fingers. In my fear and terror my degenerating body musters a last internal burst of strength, enough to wrestle him to the ground and pull the knife from his hand.

Sitting astride him, trapping him, I thrust the knife deep into his back, conquering him with a release of all the anger and pain I have ever known. As the knife penetrates skin, flesh and muscle tissue, splintering bone, he lets out the most unearthly, high-pitched, lamenting wail of orgasmic pain followed by a deep relaxed sigh and then turns to me, laying exhausted on the floor and says in a perfectly normal and matter-of-fact voice, "Was it as good for you as it was for me?"

He reaches into his pocket and pulls out a packet of cigarettes, he lights one for himself and offers me one. Drained, I cannot respond.

"You know, I'll have to give you my phone number so we can meet up again sometime."

He finishes his cigarette and jots his number on a piece of paper which he places in my hand. I remain in stunned silence. He gives me a friendly goodbye kiss on the cheek and shows himself to the door, leaving me a huddled traumatised wreck, bleeding and sick to my stomach.

46

Death rattle

Oliver Speer

The present, I hold only in contempt
For it is now and now and always now
Whereas the past embroiders on itself
With recollection's corners worn by time

The future holds its openness unwrit
It is a breath that has yet to be breathed
Or that of death; to suffocate diseased
When what was planned reveals the opposite

Now's sad stone certainty, I scrutinise
Whereas the times of joy just seem to fleet
Sit back on life, relax and close your eyes
Until nostalgia brings life back, complete

Every time I get a sore throat I get frightened, frightened that the sore throat will lead to a cough, that the cough will lead to a cold, that the cold will lead to an illness, and before I know it, I'm back in hospital with my very life in jeopardy and the sense that it was all so brief, that I could have done so much more.

I don't want to live with this morbid sense of impending doom, that at any time my body's defences could begin to deteriorate again and it would be left to my parents to pick up the pieces. They don't want to have me to worry about. They have a beautiful new granddaughter (my niece); they can't take my problems on board when she's running around and growing and getting stronger. In my niece, my sister has created something so simple yet so constructive; she has utilised the in-built drive within all creatures (sex) for its true means, to create more life.

Death rattle

I got it all wrong: sex for me became an act of self-destruction. This was never a lifestyle choice; I just never had an excuse to feel strong and happy with myself. In the light of my recent illness I feel that now I do.

Maybe I can't feel truly happy for myself and the path my life has taken, but I feel for the good of myself and those around me that I must start to approach life with a more optimistic outlook. Or else condemn myself to death. I cannot overestimate the potential of my self-destruction. I have come too close.

This piece of writing serves as a rationalising and exorcising of that self-destructive spirit. I hope it can stand on its own as something constructive, beyond my own indulgence.

June 2001

1998: Dead End

Standing on the edge of nowhere, looking on to somewhere, is where I want to be. Poised, ready to take on board any possibility, any conceivable route, this is the place where I thrive.

Today, however, I feel I have met a dead end. A dead end of inevitability, endless predictable drudgery. All the backrooms, bars and toilets call me back, mocking me with old routines of cock and suck and drug and fuck. What once started as a quest for experience, an exercising of individual freedom, has turned out to be a trap. The mind has its confines and limits: we can only reach so far, dig so deep, until we reach a mud so thick and cloying that we find ourselves stuck, and start sinking.

I have been sinking for many years now, sucked in by my own futile quest to find something beyond, something divine; driven by my own hunger and lust, a slave to my sex drive. The insecure striving for contact, to touch, to feel a part of someone else, something else, to absorb a part of everyone. And as soon as you realise no one holds the

Death rattle

answer, no one can save you, or lift you up, or guide you, you get bitter and cynical and feel powerless. You let more people fuck you up, fuck you over, fuck you, just to rub salt into the wound, just to verify your powerlessness. Not wanting to accept responsibility, it helps you to feel weak from time to time. It's easier: abandon all control to fate and for experience.

One time you ask a rough-looking skinhead to tie you up, just to see what it's like. Hog-tied, wrist to ankles, you tell him the safe word is "cunt" (easily distinguishable). When you say "cunt", whatever happens, he must stop. He inserts a finger into your anus; his hands are coarse and dry. You wince. He inserts another two fingers.

"Careful!"

"Try to relax."

Soon all his fingers are inside you; he's playing rough and your eyes start watering. He begins to make his hand into a fist. This is territory you don't want to go near.

"CUNT! ... FUCKING CUNT!" you gasp.

He just smiles and delves deeper.

"CUNT! CUNT! Pleeease! CUNT," tears running down your cheeks, unable to move, restricted by the bands bonding your wrists to your ankles, it feels like your hip is going to dislocate; agonising discomfort.

"CUUUNT!!!" He stops and slowly withdraws and unties you. Shaking and feeling physically sick, you swallow and force out a sentence, "I said 'cunt', I kept saying 'cunt'; we agreed that that was the word."

"You wanted me to go just that little bit further," he says. "Come next week you'll be thinking back to this night and having a good old wank."

Perhaps, it's too soon to tell. Shaken and wretched, I look round the room for my clothes, and gather them, unable to look my aggressor in the eye. A sock is lying in a pool of vomit.

"Fucking all time low," I think desperately, breaking for a moment through the psychotic haze of three-day

Death rattle

speed. I stand up, causing the blood to rush from my head; momentary blackout. The sensation surges over me, and with it come the memories of the evening.

The vomit is on the floor because the skinhead had wanted to vomit on my penis whilst sucking me off. Seeing as my self-destructive streak had thrown me into kamikaze experience mode, I agreed to let him, but found I had to ask him to stop after only a few seconds because the half-digested chunks tangled in my pubes made me feel sick, and my vomiting would not be wise, seeing as I hadn't eaten for three days. The skinhead obligingly urinated on me to wash the vomit off.

I had been aware of piss fetishes, but not so much vomit. Although I wasn't actively interested, I always said I'd try anything once – something to tell your grandchildren when you're in the nursing home.

2000

I started that last piece of writing, *Dead End*, two years ago with the intention of creating a short story. After those few paragraphs I had to stop as it became too painful.

I have, since the aforementioned incident, though not because of it, contracted HIV, and now find myself emaciated and languishing in a hospital bed with the tuberculosis death rattle rasping from my lungs. At one moment my body is shuddering in indescribable cold, and the next pouring out sweat like a tap, whereupon the sheets have to be changed. This happens numerous times throughout the night.

The depths of this illness are a blur. I don't remember much, except for the religious hallucinations. A bearded Jesus face will appear in the random textures of a wall, for instance, or a figure of the Virgin illuminated behind closed eyelids. For fear of becoming a self-righteous born-again Christian upon my recovery, I have to tell myself these hallucinations are merely archetypal images which every mind carries, and which are only revealed at times when the

Death rattle

mind phases out and weakens; Christianity having utilised these archetypes for its own ends.

I receive a lot of blood transfusions.

And I have hallucinated tigers: giant fluid tigers morphing from the blood bag suspended by my bed and leaping over me from left to right. This experience became so intense that I had to call for the nurse. I rang the small buzzer to the right of my bed and the nurse entered.

"I'm aware of hallucinations. I've experienced them before, but there are these giant blood tigers leaping over my bed and I'm wondering if I should do anything about it?"

The rather camp male nurse paused to think. "Is this upsetting you?"

In these sterile surroundings the hallucinations are actually a refreshing change, and, due to my altered state, the presence of the nurse was becoming stranger than they were. "It's a bit intense but I think I can cope," I reply.

"Well, I probably shouldn't give you any more drugs. If it continues, give me a bell and we'll see if we can get a doctor to have a look at you."

The tigers continued throughout the night but I decided not to bother the nurse, and in time I had fallen asleep.

In the midst of this disease I am somehow coping. When ill the human mind locks into another drive of consciousness and existence, and a lot of the self shuts down so that the body and mind can put all of their energies into the healing process.

When I was first taken ill with this illness, we thought it was only the side effects of the anti-retroviral medication I had been advised to take. It started with flu-like symptoms and problems with the circulation in my legs. For a time I could only walk with a stick, and later my walking became so pained that I had to be taken to bed at my mother's house.

My body's defences, however, had started deteriorating before I was made to take the anti-retrovirals. Although I was aware on some level that I was becoming weak, I must have been in denial, as I was still trying to keep up with my friends' drinking and partying.

Often at night, after going out to a club and consuming copious amounts of booze and ecstasy, I would find myself waking up in the warmth of my own urine. This was particularly embarrassing if I was sharing my bed with a friend, as was often the case. I clearly remember several occasions where I found myself inadvertently urinating on good friends of mine. The friends would always be polite, saying nothing of the dampness the next day. Most of the time a lot of the moisture had dried out by then anyway, as I would wake up just as I realised I was pissing, and would cuddle close to my friend in an attempt to evaporate most of the fluid with our body heat before they woke up.

For the two bedridden weeks at my mother's house, just before I was checked into hospital, I observed the breaking down of the facets of my ego.

Constantly running a fever and hallucinating, I imagined at one time six distinct characters in the bed with me, all facets of my own personality.

One was that of my sister in her youth; argumentative and bossy. Others were more literal alter egos that I had at one time consciously created. These included Geoffrey, anal yet self-destructive, insular and numb; the debauched priest or preacher; and the porn ego I created when earning some money to get through the first year of college.

I rarely feel consistent in my ego or persona, but in those first two weeks of hallucinatory sickness it seemed that all of the facets of myself were simultaneously rising to the surface, fighting it out amongst themselves in my deluded half-sleep tangle of dream and reality. It was as if I was sweating these facets of my personality out, to prepare myself for the ego-less state so important to the healing process.

My sister had become pregnant shortly after my diagnosis. She had decided to keep the baby, partly for my mother's sake, to soften the blow when she heard my bad

Death rattle

news. This was a gesture made with good intent, though I can't help feeling that the baby is to be my replacement.

My mother had given me a lift up to London to have my check up. Afterwards we had hoped to be among the first to see my newborn niece.

The doctors were amazed that I had not been checked into hospital long ago. We told them that we thought I was simply adjusting to the anti-retrovirals. They said there was no way I should be visiting a newborn baby in my condition, and promptly had me admitted as an in-patient.

Both my mother's children checked into hospital on the same day, one for matters of birth and the other, death.

... My mother feels torn between wanting to spend time with me and wanting to support my sister ...

I had been making attempts at recording the experience. Before being checked into hospital I was sketching my emaciated form, and since then have made records of my deterioration. I have also stolen a catheter and several syringes as souvenirs. I imagine I might incorporate them into an art piece if I recover; however, in my sickened, ego-less state the concept of art seems absurd, as does life in general.

This loss of self and ego is a state aspired to by many religions. The wretchedness of conscious life is at times so unbearable we do all we can do to shut off the mechanism: chanting, meditation, drugs. Sleep is rarely salvation.

My dreams offer me a mirror. When life is bad I often sleep well, only to wake to the dawning realization of the shit I'm in. Equally, when life is good with nothing to worry about, my dreams find reasons to torment me. I may wake in a cold sweat from a nightmare that the cheese in the fridge might be past its sell-by date and I haven't eaten it yet. And when I come to, and think to myself, "why am I doing this? What have I got to worry about?"

I believe that human life is tormented from the outset and that we, as human beings, will go out of our way to find problems, something to contend with, to validate our

Death rattle

torment and misery and make our existence more tangible. Do you think those millions who wept in mourning at the death of Princess Diana were really crying for a person they had never met? I believe we use these occasions as an excuse to vent our own misery and frustration; in reality we are weeping for ourselves.

In my case, at least, I find that when I have a real problem I am far more focussed, and when I don't I find myself desperately struggling to find meaning in my existence. Enveloped in this sickness, I find all my struggles and conflicts are gone. I am in that oblivious state of limbo so yearned for. I am Zen. I merely exist. My body aches but my mind is free of pain. I feel my life, so brief and insignificant, seep through my pores, and all to me is meaningless. But somehow I don't mind.

The HIV has become me. It now seems it was inevitable, like destiny. This disease is perpetuated by sexual acts, the in-built drive within all animals, though the illness has drained me of any sex drive. On one level this is quite liberating, as I can't remember the last time I went five minutes without thinking about sex. In this state sex seems the most absurd concept of them all. I wonder what a family tree of all the people who contracted HIV would look like, who fucked who and how it got to me.

HIV remains synonymous with the gay scene. It is relatively recently that homosexuality was made legal. As it existed for many years as something underground and secret, sexual encounters were often brief and anonymous, a stigma the gay scene has found hard to shake off.

The scene is full of different and unusual sexual practices. This is not because gay men are intrinsically more perverse than your average heterosexual man, but because homosexuality itself has for many years been deemed a perversion and something to be hidden away and swept under the carpet.

The gay man, on confronting his sexuality and revealing

Death rattle

his true self, will have confronted the biggest hurdle of his life. When one comes to terms with himself on this level, all minor perversions, fetishes and vices that the average heterosexual would repress will also rise to the surface. For this reason, what is underground within straight culture is mainstream within gay culture. Pretty much anything goes.

As male sexuality is very different from female sexuality, a man and a woman will often have to go through a number of social courtship rituals before they have sex. But when a man is attracted to another man, a lot of the rituals associated with heterosexual bonding and courtship can be short-circuited. Thus places exist, and have done since the beginning of time, where men can meet solely for sex.

On the surface this can seem a great idea – free sex on tap. But the gay teenager who, unaware how else to meet others like himself, naively wanders into such an environment looking for his first loving relationship, is likely to find instead, as happens all too often on the scene, that once someone's fucked you they lose interest. This often enforces the sense of isolation that many young gay men feel.

I have had a considerably high sex drive for as long as I can remember. Even as a child I was tormented by fetishistic visions and impulses that I couldn't begin to understand. From the age of being sexually active I was aware of the dangers of sex, so made sure that if I was looking for it I always carried a condom.

Things can get out of hand, though. Too many drugs – fat lines of coke – and the guy is gorgeous.

I have so much respect for him: he's an author, and older and stronger than me; he tells me I'm beautiful and he'll take care of me and that he loves me. Of course I don't believe a word of it, but I let myself get caught up in the romance of the evening; there is so much ahead. So he takes me to a club. He's on the guest list and all the drinks are free. We drop a few pills, more charlie, poppers.

Death rattle

I end up back at his flat. A grand luxurious flat with a pristine king-sized bed as the centrepiece.

This guy, before becoming a writer, first established himself in the world of gay porn. Though I can't remember the names of any of his films, his image was prolific, and on more than one occasion provided me with momentary relief from my teenage frustrations. And there I was, about to *actually* have sex with him.

Although my recollection of the night is foggy to say the least, I do remember insisting that he use a condom, and getting a strong impression that he felt put out by this request. He was not aware that I knew that he was HIV positive. When I was fifteen I had accidentally recorded a late-night TV interview with him, which I found myself rewinding repeatedly, wearing out the tape and using up a lot of tissues with it.

He says something about lubricating the inside of the condom because it feels nice. It hurts to start with, but as the drugs and poppers have loosened me up I'm soon lost in the most incredible sensations, and so am pained to tell him to stop when I sense something is wrong and soon realise that the condom is no longer there. He seems annoyed that I made him stop. Not wanting to upset him, I tell him to try again with a fresh condom. When, after a time, I find that condom to be missing as well, I become quite distressed. I tell him that I know he is positive. I remember him becoming defensive, and the atmosphere turning unpleasant and conversation awkward.

The next morning he was quick to chuck me out.

Later, when I go to the toilet, the condoms come out, entwined in my faeces. The rubberised clump won't flush, so I have to remove it by hand.

Desperately in need of advice and support I try to contact him, but only get an answering machine. I leave a message but don't hear anything back. I book myself an appointment at the clinic.

HIV is known to be present when the relevant antibodies

Death rattle

kick in. This usually takes about three months. They test me to see if I have HIV already; a week later the results arrive – negative. Three months later I'm sitting in the clinic again, waiting for results. The woman who enters is smiling, maybe a bit nervously, but a smile nonetheless. It can't be bad news.

She speaks casually, retaining her fixed grin, "Well, ... the test came back and it's positive. ... ... You are entitled to counselling. Should you fall ill you can refuse any medication if you wish. You will be asked to return monthly for a check up, only you don't come in here; you go to the clinic in the basement. ... ... Any questions?"

My friend Corrina is with me. She starts crying. I'm quite taken aback. No questions spring to mind. We go to the pub.

Hell on sea

I come from the coastal town of Hastings; the memory of the grey salt sea lingers strong in my nostrils. The seafront façades, once the height of Edwardian glamour, are now gutted crumbling shells. Down on the promenade the drunks sway and spurt obscenities, lovingly cradling their bottles of White Lightning and cans of Special Brew.

Once, when I was young, I found out that the toilets dotting the seafront were a cruising ground for queers. At the time my burgeoning sexuality, which I had not yet fully confronted, was becoming a great burden to me, the minds of most fifteen year-olds being somewhat tormented anyway. These sordid underground encounters, with old perverted pederasts and men who could not tell their families of their true nature, seemed in fitting with the guilt and shame I had long felt.

Since then all for me is out in the open and well vented. Since then the council have dotted the seafront with cameras, and so many police patrol the town that a

Death rattle

constant violation of one's privacy is taken for granted. At one time the promenade was rife with sexual encounters, smack addicts; a rainbow of debauchery. Addicts and helpless cases are moved to the town for cheap B & B and dole. Extra policing never solves the problem, it just moves it somewhere else, forces it further underground.

We once enjoyed happy hour down at Cherry's, a local bar, until someone got stabbed. The police, believing they'd got the culprit and that he was armed, raided a flat and shot dead an innocent, naked, man. After that Cherry's was closed down.

I kind of miss the fist fights and glasses flying around; cheap beer and snakebite consumed by the gallon, sustained with mountains of amphetamine.

'Hell on sea' is what the papers called Hastings after the deputy head of a local school beat his adopted daughter to death with a tent peg. Murder and rape are commonplace. The locals often talk of a curse put on the town by the occultist Alistair Crowley. The legacy of this curse being that it is difficult, if not impossible, for the town's inhabitants to ever leave. Following his death his house on the hill was burned down. Where it stood is now waste ground.

From my hospital bed I think fondly of Hastings, and wonder what keeps drawing me back to a town so choked with the stench of hopelessness, unemployment, suicide and despair – a town that is so much a part of me.

Before my illness I was arrested on the way to a squat party in London. We were just going to set up the rig when our car was pulled over. The police had me on some hash, just an eighth in my tobacco pouch), while a friend of mine was found with ketamine and a small amount of opium. We had been cooking up the K beforehand and I had written poems and slogans on the inside of the wraps, such as 'Phone your mother you filthy K-head'. These were to be read when the wrap was finished, the users having dug themselves a sizeable hole.

Death rattle

On reading these slogans one officer said to another, "What's this about then?" ... to which the other knowingly replied, ... "Trademarks," – revealing the average policeman's inept sense of humour.

I was strip searched. DNA samples, fingerprints and mug shots were taken. The police seemed quite taken aback about my HIV. "So how did you get that then?" said one officer in an arrogant and condescending tone. "Someone took advantage of me," was my curt reply. At this the officer apologised and remained silent.

On searching my pockets I was aware I had nothing to declare. Unlike the time two years earlier, when I was arrested on acid in Hastings for theft of wood for a beach party bonfire.

On that occasion, whilst in the police van, I transferred a wrap of speed from my wallet to my shoe, all the time making conversation with five police officers, a three-day cocktail of drugs coursing through my mind and body.

In the cell I learned how to meditate. Before incarceration they handed me a list of the formalities I could expect should I be tried in court, their intention being to make me stew in my own guilt. They also told me to leave my shoes (with the speed) outside my cell. I was tripping, and realised that no amount of worrying would help the situation or my future mental health, so, ignoring the list, I spent the next four hours humming an improvised mantra to accompany the infinite geometric patterns emerging from within.

"So how did you find that then?" an officer asked aggressively, before escorting me to be interviewed.

"Really good!" was my reply, "I rarely get an opportunity to meditate."

In the interview room my solicitor was more condescending than the police.

"Just admit to stealing the wood and we can go home." His voice had the tired lilt of a man who had better things to do than waste his time on idiots like me. I told him that I

Death rattle

wouldn't have taken the wood had I known it was someone's property. It had turned out to be the shutters of the building it was leaning against.

"Don't waste our time," was my solicitor's exasperated reaction.

I was encouraged to lie, saying that I knowingly stole the shutters, so that the case wouldn't go to court. I was then awarded with a caution, and, after a few photographs were taken, the guard told me I could put my shoes back on.

I remember my relief as my toes touched the wrap of speed.

I finally made it to the beach party at seven or eight a.m. A couple of friends were gathered, still tripping by the fire's last burning embers. I was offered a spliff. It tasted great.

"So this is how freedom feels."

When, as a child, I first learned to write, I wrote from right to left in mirror image. I only got as far as writing my name in this manner, as I was quickly weaned off it. This upset me because, if it was my true nature, surely it should have been encouraged. For years I imagined that perhaps, as a baby, I had been replaced by the mirror child. This would explain why I felt so different to everyone else.

At around the age of three, I would say to my mother that I wanted to die, though today I have no concept of a three year-old's knowledge of death. I had awful nightmares in which I scratched my face with my nails, sobbing and tormented. My mother would pick me up like a bundle, holding me warm and close; she'd comfort me, telling me how good Christmas would be when it comes. I'd drift back to sleep, clinging to those warm thoughts of optimism: Christmas does come round again, life does get better. It will all turn out all right.

In primary school I had few friends and did anything I could to get out of going. On more than one occasion I remember drinking shampoo to make me sick so I didn't

Death rattle

have to attend. My bowels had long been a problem. My lower intestine was distended and would not grow at the same rate as the rest of my body. This caused me great pain and frequent problems.

One such problem, anal thrush at about the age of eight, involved treatment which entailed filling a large plastic syringe with foam and injecting the foam into my anus. When the thrush had cleared I found pleasure in using the plastic syringe to inject warm water into my bowels. At that age I had no knowledge of enemas or the hidden pleasures of the rectum.

Bowel cleansing became a habit for a couple of weeks. The only problem being that the warm brown water would gush down my leg when least expected. Because of this my mother took me back to the doctor. The doctor said it was probably the side effects of the medication and should wear off after a time. For those weeks I was made to wear a sanitary towel. I also got the time off school.

Being young I knew very little of homosexuality, except that my father, who had spent some time in the marines, didn't like them. In conversation he would often associate homosexuality with paedophilia, and talked of how, when on leave, he and his mates would beat up a queer and nick his money. I have since cleared the air with him and we now get on very well. From a young age I was acutely aware that I was different. I remember praying that I wouldn't turn into one of those people my father hates.

At school I found myself experiencing strong emotions towards other boys. This, I told myself, was because I wanted to be like them. I got erections at all sorts of bizarre things I didn't understand – masculine associated things: vehicles, sports, items of clothing. This disturbed me greatly, and in my confusion I often cried myself to sleep.

Somewhere towards the end of my thirteenth year I came across a clothes catalogue belonging to my sister. All the other boys at school talked of wanking, but I had

143

Death rattle

never tried. I turned to the women's underwear section and stared intently at the models posing in skimpy lingerie, whilst mauling my genitals for stimulation. I was not getting a hard-on. Without consciously regarding what I was doing I turned to the men's section. That was when everything started happening. The sensations I was feeling were unlike anything I had experienced – a scratching of an impossible itch. In time the welling up of all my desire and frustration reached an extreme melting tension, only to explode and shoot across the room to the opposite wall.

The next sensation to pass over me was a combination of heart-sinking guilt and shame. It was now definite – I was a queer, a faggot, a homo, a poof. In my paranoid teenage mind I was everything my father, and everyone in every school and in every town, hated and wanted dead.

After that first ejaculation I had remembered one incident at the age of around ten, which I had blocked from my mind, as I couldn't make sense of it at the time.

In the excitement of play I had kissed my best friend on the cheek. In an instant the fun had turned aggressive. My friend started calling me a queer and saying I was gay (terminology I didn't associate with myself at that time). He then got some other 'friends' to hold me down and hold my legs open while he kicked me squarely and repeatedly in the balls.

Naturally I couldn't tell my school friends of my epiphany. In the school yard the word 'gay' is commonly used to describe anything crap, unworthy or insufficient. I couldn't live with this tag, so I went out of my way to have relationships with girls to prove to my friends, and to myself, that I was straight.

One day, on my way back from school, I stopped by a public toilet, as I needed a shit. I entered the graffiti-covered cubicle, dropped my pants and sat down. I had seen stuff written on toilet walls before, but being naive and paranoid I thought it was probably written by the police, or men who would beat up whoever they caught responding

Death rattle

to the messages. I reached for the toilet roll and jumped, startled. Above the toilet roll dispenser was a hole in the chipboard wall, through which was peering an eye. My heart jumped into my throat, pounding tenfold. I quickly wiped my arse, then bunked myself up onto the toilet so I could see over into the neighbouring cubicle.

What I saw was a fat middle-aged man in tweed, with a flat cap, hurriedly adjusting his fly. I didn't know for how long he'd been watching me, but from his flushed expression I knew he'd been masturbating. Experiencing a rush of nausea through my whole body, I darted out of the toilet and ran all the way home.

From the age of fourteen I masturbated compulsively, often three or four times a day, just to get the lustful thoughts out of my head, to calm the demon. At that age I also went for long walks of an evening along the seafront.

My first sexual experience was at about this age. I was reading the writing on a toilet cubicle along the Marina when I heard a man enter to urinate. He had been standing by the urinals for some time when I heard his feet move towards my cubicle. He made two pronounced snorting noises. I had not seen what he looked like, but through curiosity I emulated his noises, to which he coughed. This I also repeated. I had seen it written on the wall that this kind of communication is common practice, though I was quite taken aback when the door of my cubicle opened.

The man who stood before me was plain-looking, probably in his mid-thirties, with a slim, almost skinny build. He whispered in a rasping voice, "I know a place where we can go."

My heart was beating fast and the feeling of nausea was there, but at the same time I felt somewhat exhilarated.

"Okay."

He left the cubicle looking behind at me and I nervously followed. We walked for quite some time. He asked my name and if I had a boyfriend. I told him I had a girlfriend.

"I meet lots like you."

Death rattle

We finally reached a beach hut further up the beach. He said it belonged to a friend. He unlocked the door of the whitewashed shack. It had no lights, the floor was damp and there was no furniture, so we had to stand. He kissed me; his flesh and saliva felt cold and reptilian. He slowly unzipped my fly and reached inside. I was erect; his hand felt clammy.

When, after some fumbling, I ejaculated, the horror of what I was doing came over me. I quickly made my excuses and left. I retched at the thought of what I had done and couldn't spit enough to get his taste out of my mouth.

I would return to the seafront sporadically as the months passed. I was very depressed, and the bad sex somehow made me feel better about my depression – it gave it a reason and validated it. At that time I toyed with lame suicide attempts; I also cut myself.

On one rare occasion I actually met an attractive boy of about my age. He told me he was straight and he just wanted someone to suck him off. All I wanted was to kiss him and hold him and lie with him. He told me I couldn't kiss him; he just wanted his cock sucked. It was shaped like a banana.

After leaving school and at age seventeen, coming-out to my friends and mother, I had some brief relationships.

These often consisted of straight boys who wanted to experiment but who, when it came down to it, were really straight, and so fucked with my emotions. Or boys who were probably really gay but had girlfriends, so our encounters were sworn to secrecy lest anyone find out. These all seemed in some way tainted with self-destruction and self-loathing, often not on my part.

One boy, who I realise in retrospect, I was in love with, claimed to be very suicidal. I didn't believe him as he was something of a faker; he went through religions like shirts. I called his bluff saying, "If you're going to do it, do it properly. Try two techniques at once: take some pills and hang yourself."

Death rattle

We split up after a time. He was found a month later in his hometown, hung by the neck. He had also taken an overdose.

Fade out

These memories come back to me in hospital. I am in quarantine so there's not much else to think about. I have got very good at shutting off my mind and staring at the wall for hours, as I can't seem to tune in the TV. It would only be mindless trivia anyway. I feel I must soak up this experience. I have started to decline my three-hourly fix of codeine.

Many medications have been tried and failed, including *Septrin*, a drug that, when drip-fed, felt as its name sounds – a septic acid burning through my veins, causing the needle entry points to get infected, leaving me with sores up my arms. At first they thought I had pneumonia, then PCP, which I thought was a drug, then they decided I had tuberculosis. It was a relief when they stopped the *Septrin*, but I did not anticipate what was to replace it.

The tuberculosis and anti-retroviral medication I have been prescribed consists of over twenty pills, ranging from small ones to what looks like a horse tranquilliser. I have to take these pills before breakfast.

I am often sick, and as a result am made to take them again. My throat is raw with bile and the dry scrape of numerous tablets. On top of this, most of the veins in my arms have collapsed due to the constant drip-feeds and injections. This has caused my gaunt limbs to take on a bluish hue, dotted with purple-yellow bruises.

On one occasion the nurse came to give me an injection, I felt the needle enter the vein then exit into the wasted muscle on the other side. Despite my whimpers of protest the nurse proceeded to empty the syringe into my flesh. My arm ached in agony, a swollen purple balloon that felt like it might fall off.

Death rattle

The doctor has ordered me another chest x-ray, about the fifth in as many weeks. I am wheeled there as I am wheeled everywhere. The only exercise I get is the walk to the toilet, and due to this I have now fully lost the use of my legs. On the way to x-ray, waiting for the elevator, a young girl of about five or six stares at me in my wheelchair, oxygen cylinder and mask attached. I can sense she is frightened; I must look pretty scary. My eyes and cheekbones are sunken and my frame has the gauntness of death. I stare back at her and hold my gaze, watching her shiver in terror as if she is about to cry. Her parents pull her away.

Outside x-ray I keep nodding off. With no space to rest in my wheelchair, my head rolls back and I awaken with a start.

The results show my heart has got bigger. I make some joke, such as, "Does that mean I'm a more loving person?"

The doctors mumble a wry chuckle in response. "It seems your heart has got infected. The sack that surrounds it has inflated with fluid to fight off the infection."

I was not surprised. My heartbeats had been pained and my breathing shallow. I was told the fluid had to be drained as soon as possible.

The next day I had an appointment to see the surgeon. I had to have the last slot in the day to prevent my TB from being passed to any other patients. I was supposed to be starved of food and water for twelve long hours beforehand, but as the appointment was put back it was more like twenty. I don't mind the lack of food, as I haven't been eating anyway, but the lack of fluids is unbearable, as I've been on oxygen for days, which tends to dry out your mouth.

I am wheeled into a room and surrounded by surgeons and medical students. I am told my condition is rare, and that the procedure I require involves draining off the fluid constricting my heart through a tube fed underneath my ribcage. This, I am told, is a risky procedure, and so I must

Death rattle

sign legal forms accepting the possibility of death. One of the students asks how old I am.

"Twenty two."

"You're so young, it's such a shame," she says, enforcing the sense of impending doom.

I am placed on a foam wedge and given an injection of local anaesthetic. My heart is visible on the monitor above my head. I am disinfected. The surgeon explains that he will make a small incision through which a wire will be fed. This wire will be visible on the monitor as it cuts its way to my heart. When it hooks in place the tube can be fed in, ready to drain the fluid.

"If my heart stops beating and you have to prize open my ribcage, will I still be conscious?" I enquire, only half jokingly.

"It's not funny. ... You mustn't speak like that." snaps the surgeon.

I am awake for the whole process, and can see it all taking place. In spite of the local anaesthetic I can feel the incision and every move the wire makes.

I watch in the monitor as the end of the wire hooks in place between the sack containing the fluid and my heart. The surgeon attaches a large syringe and starts syringing out the fluid. It is green-yellow in colour, like pungent urine. Each syringe is put aside to be sent to a laboratory. After a few I ask if it's nearly finished.

"We've only just started." the surgeon says.

Syringe after syringe after syringe is set aside. I can literally feel the pressure being released from around my heart. When the procedure is finished I ask the surgeon how much fluid there was.

"About two litres," he replies. "That's the same as two cartons of orange juice."

I have to sleep for two nights with the tube attached and a bag draining any remaining fluid. Every time my heart beats I can feel the wire scratching against it.

I often carry with me the burden that the whole path

149

Death rattle

I took from my teenage years, away from my mother, to whom I felt very close, was some search for conflict; a stirring-up of my boring, middle class, middle of the road life; to give myself a cause, something to feel passionate about, something that matters.

From this point I threw myself into wretched experiences – a mental self-mutilation. Drugs, sex, dressing like a freak, getting beaten up and going out even weirder the next night to show I didn't care, and getting beaten up again, when really I did care. I was an emotional wreck.

I'd find myself doing things like missing the last train from London and sleeping rough with a bunch of crack addicts, and a boy prostitute, who helped me out for a time, but when he needed his next fix he nicked off with all the money I had.

And I start to wonder: did I create this shit to have something to do, to think about, to talk about? At least misery can cut through the numb and endless boredom; conflict can validate and bring life to any dull existence. Have I all this time been picking away at myself, killing myself little by little, because I haven't got the guts to get it over with in one fell swoop?

Back in my hospital bed I am surrounded by papers and pens, desperately trying to document my downfall, to make sense of it all, to account for this life's filtering out, clinging on to desperate strands. The nurses wonder why I'm writing and drawing.

"It' ll put too much of a strain on your mind," they say.

I really don't know why myself. From the perspective of this illness my creative ego seems absurd. Why do I perform these strange dances? Why do I document this sinking ship? For sentiment? To leave a legacy? Why did the cameraman keep filming when the Hindenburg went up in flames? My downfall isn't nearly as spectacular.

Perhaps all along I was subconsciously constructing elaborate plans for my own death, the greatest show.

Appendices

appendix 1 **Glossary**

3TC   Code for Lamuvidine. See NRTI.

Abacavir   See NRTI.

AIDS   Acquired Immunodeficiency Syndrome. Condition where the body can no longer fight off even the smallest infection, leading to multiple symptoms, disability and death. This is the condition that HIV eventually leads to.

Amprenavir   See protease inhibitor (PI).

antibody   Protein substance produced by the immune system to 'mark' harmful substances in response to infection.

asymptomatic   Whilst affected by a disease or condition, not experiencing any symptoms.

AZT   Code originally used for Zidovudine. See NRTI. This was the first drug shown to be effective against HIV

anti-retroviral   Drug or substance that acts against retroviruses such as HIV.

bacteria   Small micro-organism (a complete cell) sometimes referred to as a germ.

CD4   A protein on the surface of T-Cells that is measured (counted) in blood tests and used as an indicator of the number of viable T-Cells in the body. A healthy person would have a count between 800 and 1,200; a person with AIDS typically between 0 and 200.

CMV   Cytomegalovirus. Member of herpes virus family. Suppressed in healthy people but in immunosupressed people it reproduces unchecked and leads to blindness.

Combination   Also known as 'combination therapy' or HAART.   Combination of 3, 4 or more drugs used to control the virus and minimise risk of resistance due to mutation.

ddC   Code for zalcitabine. See NRTI.

ddI   Code for Didianosine. See NRTI.

Delaviridine   See NNRTI.

Didianosine   See NRTI.

appendix 1   **Glossary**

DLA   Disability Living Allowance. Social security Benefit given to severely sick or disabled people to assist them in managing their daily living needs.

DNA   deoxyribonucleic acid. Carries genetic information comprising blocks of amino acids, in the cells of all living things.

Efavirenz   See NNRTI.

epididymo-orchitis   Infection of the coiled tubes in the scrotum. The tubes store and transport sperm.

genetic information   Instructions that tell a cell exactly what to do, e.g. DNA, RNA or enzymes.

HAART   highly active anti-retroviral therapy

Hepatitis   Inflammation and/or damage to liver, caused by disease, alcohol abuse or medication side effects.

Hep C   Hepatitis 'C'. Potentially fatal viral disease of the liver that is slow acting and difficult to treat.

HHV-8   human herpes virus type 8. Type of herpes virus (similar to virus that causes shingles, cold sores and chicken pox). Probably transmitted orally. Suppressed in healthy person. Can multiply out of control and cause KS in severely immunosupressed individuals or those with AIDS.

HIV   The human immunodeficiency virus. A retrovirus with 9 genes that specifically attack human T-Cells.

HTLV3   Human T-lymphocyte virus type 3. Original name of HIV. From 1987 HIV was the preferred name.

Hydroxyurea   Anti-HIV drug of ribonucleotide reductase inhibitors group of anti-HIV drugs. Also used in the treatment of Cancers. The drawback: it inhibits the bone marrow, suppressing the production of blood cells.

immune system   The body's system for fighting off infection, comprising bone marrow, spleen, lymphatic system and white blood cells among others.

Immunocompromised   When the immune system is so weak that it cannot fight off infection.

Immunosupressed   When the immune system is weakened by disease (e.g. HIV) or drugs or external influences.

Indinavir   See protease inhibitor (PI).

Integrase   An enzyme that HIV uses to insert its genetic material into an infected cell

KS   Kaposi's Sarcoma.   A type of cancer causing lesions on the skin or internal organs, often associated with AIDS. Found to be associated with the human herpes virus–8 (HHV-8).

Lamuvidine   Code 3TC. See NRTI

Lipodystrophy   Side effect of anti-HIV medication and HIV itself where fat is lost from the upper body (giving gaunt faces) and limbs but is moved into the body cavity giving fatty humps on the back (widows hump or camel hump), enlarged belly/hip area, or breast enlargement (in men and women).

Log Scale   A system where numbers are expressed as the Log10 of the measurement.   e.g. 10 equals 1.00,   50 = 1.70,   100 equals 2.00,   1,000 equals 3.00 etc.

Lopinavir   See protease inhibitor (PI).

Lymphocyte   A type of white blood cell.

MAC   Mycobacterium avium complex. The name used for MAI in the US.

MAI   Mycobacterium avium intracellulare.   Bacterial infection that affects the liver, spleen, lymphatic system and bone marrow particularly of people affected by AIDS. Mycobacterium avium and mycobacterium intracellulare are very similar bacteria that are usually grouped together.   Often found in the soil, water and food. Rarely affect people with healthy immune systems. Belong to the same family as the organism that causes TB (mycobacterium tuberculosis).

Mutation   Every time a virus reproduces there is a chance that random errors are made in the gene sequence copy. Most of these will result in a dead virus however occasionally a viable virus is created that is different in its structure and abilities from its parent wild type virus.

Nelfinavir   See protease inhibitor (PI).

Neuropathy   Damage to the nerve fibres caused by either the HIV virus itself and/or the side effects of anti-HIV medication (particularly NRTI's).   Manifests itself on the peripheral nerves first hence 'peripheral neuropathy'. Symptoms are loss of sensation with shooting pains and a continual cold feeling.

Nevirapine   See NNRTI.

Night Sweat   A common side effect of HIV infection where the body sweats very heavily at night even though the body is at normal temperature in and attempt to fight off the virus.

NNRTI   Non-nucleoside reverse transcriptase inhibitor. Anti-HIV drug that stops HIV from using reverse transcriptase but not by mimicking a nucleoside. In many cases the exact way they inhibit reverse transcriptase is unknown. Group includes: **Delaviridine, Efavirenz** and **Nevirapine.**

NRTI   Nucleoside reverse transcriptase inhibitor or nucleoside analogue.   Anti-HIV drug that stops HIV from using reverse transcriptase by mimicking a nucleoside. Also used for treatment of viral hepatitis.   Group includes: **Abacavir, Didianosine** (code: **ddI**), **Lamuvidine** (code: **3TC**), **Nevirapine, zalcitabine** (code: **ddC**) and **Zidovudine** (code: **AZT** or **ZDV**) Zidovudine was the first anti-HIV drug.

Nucleoside   One of the amino acid building blocks used to form DNA and RNA

Nucleoside analogue   Anti-HIV drug that stops HIV from using reverse transcriptase by mimicking a nucleoside building block

Nucleotide Analogue   Anti-HIV drug that stops HIV from using reverse transcriptase by mimicking a nucleoside building block.   They differ from nucleoside analogues in that they do not have to be converted (phosphorylated) within the cell to reach their active form. Group includes Tenofovir

Opportunistic Infection   A specific infection that takes the opportunity of a damaged immune system to attack.

Osteoporosis   Condition where the bones become brittle due to lack of calcium. Normally associated with older women but also affects people with HIV.

PCP   Pneumocystis carinii pneumonia.   Type of pneumonia particularly associated with AIDS

Peripheral Neuropathy   See neuropathy.

Primates   A generic term for apes, baboons, chimpanzees, gorillas and monkeys

Protease   An enzyme used by HIV as part of its reproductive cycle. Protease 'cuts' large proteins into the smaller proteins from which the new viral particles are produced. New HIV particles produced in the presence of protease inhibitors are immature and non-infectious

Protease Inhibitor   An anti HIV drug that stops HIV from using protease and so affects its ability to reproduce. Group includes: **Amprenavir, Indinavir, Lopinavir, Nelfinavir, Ritonavir** and **Saquinavir.**

Resistance   Due to mutations the virus becomes immune to the effects of a particular drug, normally caused when the amount of virus is high and the level of medication in the body is too low to stop viral replication

Retrovirus   Retroviruses are infectious particles consisting of an RNA genome packaged in a protein capsid, surrounded by a lipid envelope. This lipid envelope contains polypeptide chains including receptor-binding proteins which link to the membrane receptors of the host cell, initiating the process of infection. Retroviruses contain RNA as the hereditary material in place of the more common DNA. In addition to RNA retrovirus particles also contain the enzyme reverse transcriptase (or RNAse), which causes synthesis of a complementary DNA molecule (cDNA) using virus RNA as a template. When a retrovirus infects a cell, it injects its RNA into the cytoplasm of that cell along with the reverse transcriptase enzyme. The cDNA produced from the RNA template contains the virally derived genetic instructions and allows infection of the host cell to proceed.

Reverse Transcriptase An Enzyme that is used by viruses to build new copies from RNA they have made during replication.

Ribonucleotide reductase inhibitor an anti-HIV drug that stops HIV from using reverse transcriptase by reducing the supply of ribonucleotide reductase, a human enzyme which is used to produce proteins called dNTPs, which in turn form the building blocks of viral DNA. By blocking ribonucleotide reductase, depletes the pool of dNTPs, thus hindering HIV reproduction. This group includes hydroxyurea

Ritonavir See protease inhibitor (PI).

RNA Ribonucleic acid. Complex nucleic acid responsible for the transmission of genetic material

Saquinavir See protease inhibitor (PI).

Septrin Antibiotic used as prophylaxis (prevention) of diseases associated with AIDS particularly MAI and PCP.

Seroconversion The time at which a person's antibody status changes i.e. the time at which the body becomes aware that it is infected.

Symptomatic Affected by a disease or condition, and experiencing symptoms.

T-Cell A type of white blood cell that identifies foreign organisms. The cell that is attacked by the HIV virus.

T-Lymphocyte See T-Cell.

Tenofovir Anti-HIV drug of the nucleotide analogue group.

Tuberculosis A bacterial infection (mycobacterium

tuberculosis) that attacks the lungs a major worldwide health problem in its own right that is particularly damaging and difficult to treat in HIV affected people.

Viral Load   The amount of virus in the body is measured and counted as copies per ml of blood, as a virus multiplies so rapidly and in such numbers with one virus leading to the creation of 5-50 new viruses in one step a logarithmic (log) scale is used. When HAART medication is used the aim is to keep this as low as possible and ideally below the level that virus can be detected (although the virus is still present), a person with HIV and a viral load of up to 50,000 would probably not need to commence treatment unless their CD4 is below 250 whereas a viral load of 300,000 and above would be considered very serious.

Viral Replication   Virus containing viral material (RNA and several copies of reverse transcriptase ((DNA polymerase) (for a retrovirus)) or DNA for a virus. After infecting a cell, the reverse transcriptase is used to make the initial copies of viral DNA from viral RNA. Once a DNA strand has been synthesized, a complementary viral DNA strand is made. These double strand copies of viral DNA are inserted into the host-cell chromosome and host-cell RNA polymerase is used to make virus-related RNA. These RNA strands serve as templates for making new copies of the viral chromosomal RNA and serve also as mRNA. mRNA is translated into viral proteins that are used to make the virus envelope. New viral particles are assembled, bud from the plasma membrane, and are released.

Virus   Small package of DNA designed to infect a host cell and make that cell make more copies of the original virus. It is only capable of reproduction within a host cell.

Wild Type Virus   Virus that has not previously been exposed to drugs and so has not undergone mutation.

Zalcitabine   see **ddC**

ZDV   see **AZT**

appendix 2

Writers and their works

Benz   In a normal day.

Chris   My mate Ritchie.

Eliza   Life, TB and HIV – the devil's alliance.

Evangelisto, Marcello
Aurora of yore although it is fall, The fall.

Greening, P J   A difficult day.

Hamilton, Graham   It's you that counts.

Hanuman, Andrew   Back to work, Bloody Valentine,
The dancing shaman, Insomnia, It's a sick world,
The leather bar, My travelling companion, Sanctuary,
Voodoo.

host, a   These things.

Jones, Peter Kim Lee   The journey.

Jude   Survivor.

Lalopoulous, Emmanuel   If you're not gonna kill me,
Superman; So.

Mark   My heroine.

Nelson, Mike   Aids is just a name, Death comes
to us, Definition of life and love, It came, A move
forwards, The ribbon song, The sounds of summer,
Still waters, World AIDS Day.

Painton, Guy   Millennium Bug.

Pual   Hope and remembrance.

pretty boy, a   A stench I cannot forget, Victim.

Roberts, Antony   Normal is what you're used to.

RV   A paean to HIV.

Speer, Oliver   Death Rattle, Just a dream,
Of sacrilege and sodomy, Poem after Rimbaud,
Pseudo masochism?, Septic leg.

Spleen, Oliver   Literary pseudonym of Oliver Speer.

Thomas, Richard   Return to sender.

William   Reflections of the past.

My mate Ritchie © Chris;
published in *+VE* magazine April 2002.

My travelling companion © Hanuman, Andrew 1998.

Normal is what you're used to © Roberts, Antony.

A paean to HIV © RV;
published in *+VE* magazine April 2002.

Poem after Rimbaud © Speer, Oliver 2002.

Pseudo masochism? © Speer, Oliver 1997;
published in *A necrophiliac's quiche.*

Reflections of the past © William

Return to sender © Thomas, Richard

The ribbon song © Nelson, Mike;
published in *+VE* magazine December 2002.

Of sacrilege and sodomy © Speer, Oliver;
published in *+VE* magazine April 2002

Sanctuary © Hanuman, Andrew 2002.

Septic leg © Speer, Oliver 2002.

So © Lalopoulos, Emmanuel

The sounds of summer © Nelson, Mike.

A stench I cannot forget © a pretty boy.

Still waters © Nelson, Mike.

Survivor © Jude;
published in *+VE* magazine September 2002.

TB and HIV – the devil's alliance © Eliza

These things © a host;
published in *+VE* magazine March 2002

Victim © a pretty boy.

Voodoo © Hanuman, Andrew;
published in *Four seasons in a day* June 2003.

World AIDS Day © Nelson, Mike;
published in *+VE* magazine December 2002

appendix 4

Reprints

T-Cell Chronicles

your choice of
- excerpts
- single article or story
- selection of articles or stories
- the complete book

formats
- same size   (110mm x 178mm)
- large print (150mm x 243mm)

bindings
- sheets, or bound as books or booklets

no minimum quantities
- Order just the right quantity you need, just when you want it.   Using on-demand printing and publishing avoids producing and stocking material that is never used.

permissions
- All copyright material subject to permission from and terms of the copyright owners.

Open Door
35 Camelford Street, Brighton BN2 1TQ
TELEPHOne   **(01273) 605706**   FAX: **(01273) 624044**

appendix 5

Documentation & communications

documentation

- editing
- typesetting
- illustration
- digital printing
- design
- book binding
- development of presentations and publications

Information processed to create and produce products for sending out the right messages at the right time.

- briefing notes
- reports
- updates
- resource material for training, awareness projects, campaigns and marketing
- loose-leaf or bound books for internal circulation or public access.

data dissemination

Material distributed to individuals or groups on demand or scheduled. Using on-demand publishing and printing reduces waste from producing and stocking material that is never used.

stationery

Stationery and supporting material designed and produced to enhance document creativity and impact.

envelopes & packaging

Envelopes and packaging to optimise communications function, and document delivery.

OMNIGEN

Curtis House, 34 Third Avenue
Hove, East Sussex BN3 2PD

TELEPHONE 01273 747183   FAX 01273 776129

about **Open Door**

**Open Door is a safe
and supportive place for
people living with HIV**

Wide range of practical and emotional support services – drop-in, by appointment or in the community – for men and women who are HIV positive and live in Brighton & Hove.

services we offer

- appointments
- lunch (£1.00 donation)
- one-to-one support
- information and referrals
- money & welfare rights advice
- health promotion advice
- specialist women's services
- charitable grant applications
- volunteering opportunities

- drop-in
- coffee, tea
- peer support
- computer access

- condoms, lube

- in-house groups

staff and who we are

The paid staff team is supported by a team of committed volunteers.

Open Door is a Chichester Diocesan project under the auspices of the Social Responsibility Department. The Chichester Diocesan Fund and Board of Finance (inc.) is a registered charity No. 243134

confidentiality

We operate a strict confidentiality policy which applies to staff, volunteers, service users and visitors.

equal opportunities

We are committed to equal opportunities for all, and to supporting and promoting choices and rights for HIV positive people.

access to other agencies

Staff from these agencies provide information, support and referrals, either at drop-in clinics or by appointment:

√ **Community Nurse Specialist Team** – medical and nursing support services in the community

√ **Social Care & Health Specialist Team** – advice and information about HIV and social care issues for positive people and their carers

√ **Housing Office** – specialist advice and support around housing issues

for more information

about these and other services phone or visit us.

days open   Monday – Friday 10.00 am – 4.00 pm
days closed   Saturday, Sunday & bank holidays
drop-in   11.30 am – 2.30 pm
lunch served   1.00 pm – 2.30 pm
appointmets   We are open for appointments outside these hours

Open Door

VISIT   **35 Camelford Street, Brighton BN2 1TQ**
TELEPHONE   **(01273) 605706**   FAX: **(01273) 624044**

appendix 7

Acknowledgements

Scarman Trust – Can Do Grant
Without their support, both financial and practical, this publication could not have been possible.

+ve magazine
Providing an outlet for the group's work, and for their continued support and encouragement.

Open Door
Staff Team, volunteers and service users

Shaun Levin
Creative involvement

Brighton & Hove Primary Care Trust

**Brighton & Hove City Council,
Social Care & Health**

G Scene magazine

The Argus newspaper

Diocese of Chichester
For continued support.

Friends, family and partners of the writers
Without their support on a daily basis nothing would be possible.